Ace your GCSE D&T exam with CGP!

Drawing up plans for a top grade in GCSE Design and Technology?
You've come to the right place — this fantastic CGP book is packed with
exam-style practice to help make sure you're 100% ready for the real thing!

There are hundreds of realistic questions covering every topic you'll need to
know for the AQA exam, from textiles and timber to folding and moulding.

We've also included plenty of info about your assessments and helpful
tips to help you keep up your quality control in the exams!

CGP — still the best! ☺

Our sole aim here at CGP is to produce the highest quality books —
carefully written, immaculately presented and dangerously close to being funny.

Then we work our socks off to get them out to you
— at the cheapest possible prices.

Contents

✓ Use the tick boxes to check off the topics you've completed.

Section Five — Wood, Metals and Polymers

Section Six — Textiles

Section Seven — Electronic and Mechanical Systems

Section Eight — Designing and Making

Section Nine — Mixed Questions

Published by CGP

Editors:
Christopher Lindle, Camilla Simson and Ethan Starmer-Jones.

Contributor:
Debbie McGrory

Consultant:
Ryan Ball

Proofreaders:
Anne Ainsworth, Frances Rooney, David Ryan and Hayley Thompson.

With thanks to Ana Pungartnik for the copyright research.

ISBN: 978 1 78294 753 0

Printed by Elanders Ltd, Newcastle upon Tyne.
Clipart from Corel®

How to Use This Book

- Hold the book <u>upright</u>, approximately <u>50 cm</u> from your face, ensuring that the text looks like <u>this</u>, not s̅i̅ɥ̅ʇ̅. Alternatively, place the book on a <u>horizontal</u> surface (e.g. a table or desk) and sit adjacent to the book, at a distance which doesn't make the text too small to read.

- In case of emergency, press the two halves of the book together <u>firmly</u> in order to close.

- Before attempting to use this book, familiarise yourself with the following <u>safety information</u>:

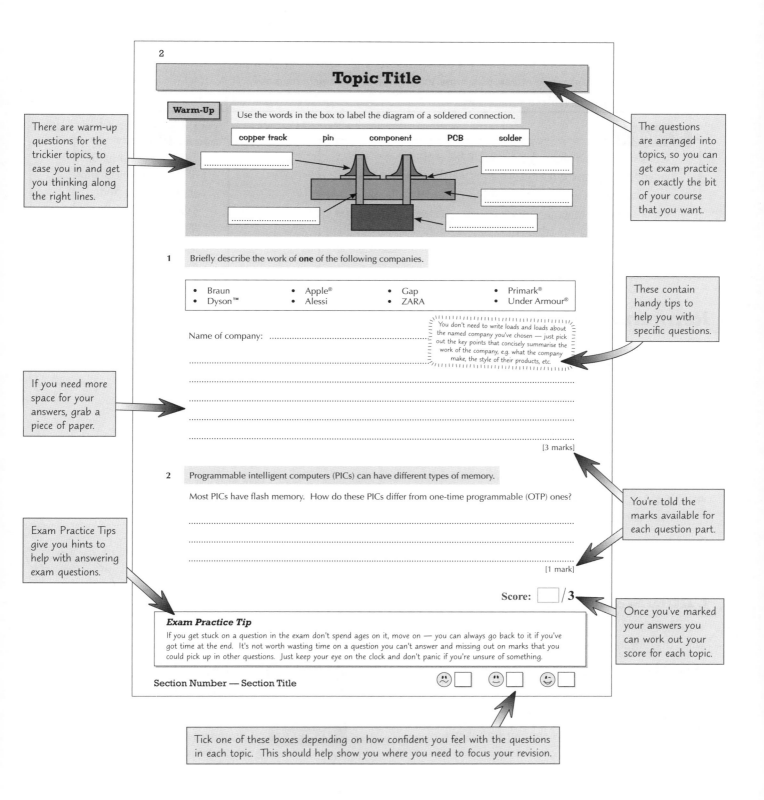

Exam Technique

Here's What to Expect in the Exam

1) At the end of your GCSE Design and Technology course you'll have to sit an exam. It's worth <u>50%</u> of your <u>total mark</u>. The exam is worth <u>100 marks</u> and is <u>2 hours</u> long.

2) The questions in the exam will test you on <u>all areas</u> of the <u>course</u>. The exam is split into <u>three sections</u> which test you on different parts of the course. Each section contains different <u>types of questions</u>:

Section A

- Consists of a mixture of <u>multiple choice questions</u>, worth <u>one mark</u> each, and <u>short answer</u> questions.
- The multiple choice questions have one correct answer and three incorrect answers. Only pick <u>one</u> answer — if you pick more than one you won't get the mark.
- <u>20 marks</u> are available in <u>total</u>.

Section B

- Consists of a few <u>short answer</u> questions and one <u>extended response</u> question, which is worth more marks.
- Some questions may offer a <u>choice</u> on what to write about — e.g. a choice of <u>materials</u>, <u>products</u>, etc. It's worth spending a moment <u>reading</u> the <u>whole question</u> to figure out which option to choose — pick the one you could write the <u>best answer</u> for.
- <u>30 marks</u> are available in <u>total</u>.

Section C

- Consists of a mixture of questions including <u>short answers</u> and <u>extended response</u> questions.
- <u>50 marks</u> are available in <u>total</u>.

Remember These Tips

1) <u>Always</u> read every question <u>carefully</u>.
   Don't write an essay about modelling if it's asking about developing prototypes.

2) Use the number of <u>marks</u> as a <u>guide</u> on <u>how much</u> to <u>write</u>.
   Try to write a point for each mark. For example, if the question's worth 3 marks, write 3 points — not just a single sentence.

3) Write your answers <u>clearly</u>, using <u>good grammar</u>, <u>spelling</u> and <u>punctuation</u>.
   If the examiner can't read your answer, you won't get any marks, even if it's right.

4) Use the correct <u>terminology</u>.
   Know your technical terms — CMYK, MDF, PIC... you can't write about these if you don't know what they mean.

5) Make your <u>sketches clear</u>.
   Draw clearly and label your sketches — it makes it easier for the examiner to see what you're trying to get across.

6) <u>Don't panic</u>.
   If you really can't do a question, just leave it and move on to the next one. You can come back to it at the end.

Understand the Command Words

Questions will often use <u>command words</u> — these words tell you <u>how</u> to answer the question. If you <u>don't know</u> what they mean, you might not answer the question <u>properly</u>. Here are some you might come across:

State   You should give a <u>short answer</u> or <u>list</u> — you don't need to explain why.

Define   You should give a <u>clear</u>, <u>precise</u> meaning of the word or phrase.

Outline You should give a <u>brief summary</u> of a process.

Explain You should <u>give reasons</u> to show <u>why</u>.

Describe You should give a <u>detailed description</u> of something.

Discuss You should make a <u>balanced argument</u> covering a range of opinions.

Assess / Evaluate You should use <u>evidence</u> and your <u>own knowledge</u> to come to a <u>conclusion</u>.

Exam Technique

Plan Out Your Answer to Extended Response Questions

Extended response questions are longer questions worth 6 or more marks and with a scary number of dotted lines underneath... They often use command words like discuss, evaluate or assess (see previous page).

1) Your answer must be well-written (good spelling, grammar and punctuation) and well-structured.

2) Before you start an extended response question, jot down the points you want to make and plan your answer to help structure it well and avoid repeating things.

3) You might have to weigh up the advantages and disadvantages of something, or cover both sides of an argument then form your own opinion.

4) Make absolutely sure you're answering the question and not just waffling on.

Here's an example:

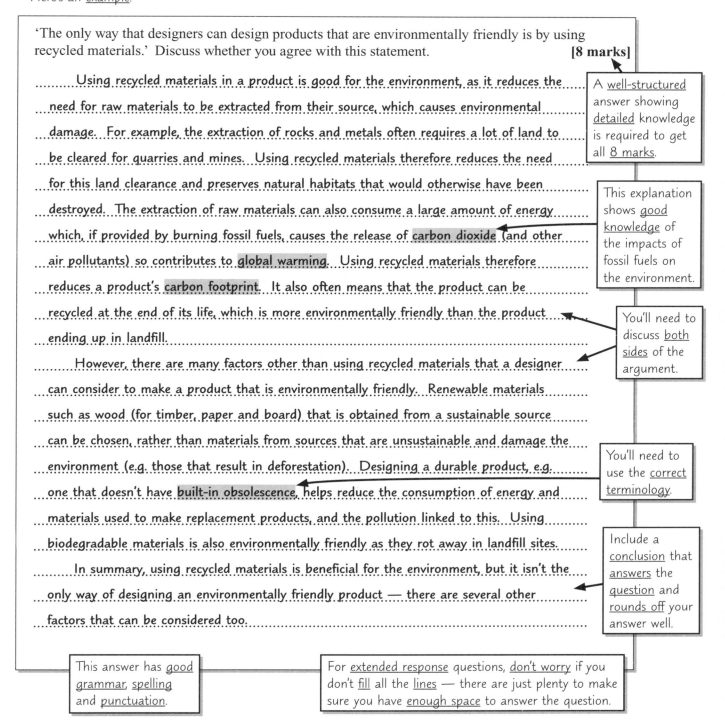

'The only way that designers can design products that are environmentally friendly is by using recycled materials.' Discuss whether you agree with this statement. **[8 marks]**

Using recycled materials in a product is good for the environment, as it reduces the need for raw materials to be extracted from their source, which causes environmental damage. For example, the extraction of rocks and metals often requires a lot of land to be cleared for quarries and mines. Using recycled materials therefore reduces the need for this land clearance and preserves natural habitats that would otherwise have been destroyed. The extraction of raw materials can also consume a large amount of energy which, if provided by burning fossil fuels, causes the release of carbon dioxide (and other air pollutants) so contributes to global warming. Using recycled materials therefore reduces a product's carbon footprint. It also often means that the product can be recycled at the end of its life, which is more environmentally friendly than the product ending up in landfill.

However, there are many factors other than using recycled materials that a designer can consider to make a product that is environmentally friendly. Renewable materials such as wood (for timber, paper and board) that is obtained from a sustainable source can be chosen, rather than materials from sources that are unsustainable and damage the environment (e.g. those that result in deforestation). Designing a durable product, e.g. one that doesn't have built-in obsolescence, helps reduce the consumption of energy and materials used to make replacement products, and the pollution linked to this. Using biodegradable materials is also environmentally friendly as they rot away in landfill sites.

In summary, using recycled materials is beneficial for the environment, but it isn't the only way of designing an environmentally friendly product — there are several other factors that can be considered too.

A well-structured answer showing detailed knowledge is required to get all 8 marks.

This explanation shows good knowledge of the impacts of fossil fuels on the environment.

You'll need to discuss both sides of the argument.

You'll need to use the correct terminology.

Include a conclusion that answers the question and rounds off your answer well.

This answer has good grammar, spelling and punctuation.

For extended response questions, don't worry if you don't fill all the lines — there are just plenty to make sure you have enough space to answer the question.

Exam Technique

Technology in Manufacturing

1   Which **one** of the following statements about automation is **not** true?

     A   Automation can increase the efficiency of manufacturing. ☐

     B   Automation is the use of machines to carry out tasks automatically. ☐

     C   Automation can be used to manufacture a whole product. ☐

     D   Automation always requires a lot of input from humans. ☐

                                                        [1 mark]

2   Robots are used in many modern factories.

   a)   State **two** reasons why a company might choose to use robots rather than humans
        in manufacturing.

       1. ....

       ....

       2. ....

       ....

                                                        [2 marks]

   b)   Give **one** reason why robots aren't always able to replace human workers in manufacturing.

       ....

       ....

                                                        [1 mark]

3   Which **one** of the following is an approach to manufacturing designed to
      minimise the amount of resources used and waste produced?

     A   Computer aided manufacturing ☐

     B   Lean manufacturing ☐

     C   Computer aided design ☐

     D   Flexible manufacturing ☐

                                                        [1 mark]

4   Give **two** advantages of using a Just-In-Time (JIT) system.

       1. ....

       ....

       2. ....

       ....

                                                        [2 marks]

Score: ☐ **/7**

☺ ☐   ☺ ☐   ☺ ☐

Production Systems — CAD/CAM

1 Which **one** of the following is a process of designing products using a computer?

- **A** CAM ☐
- **B** CNC ☐
- **C** CAD ☐
- **D** 3D printing ☐

[1 mark]

2 **Figure 1** shows a cardboard net for sandwich packaging.

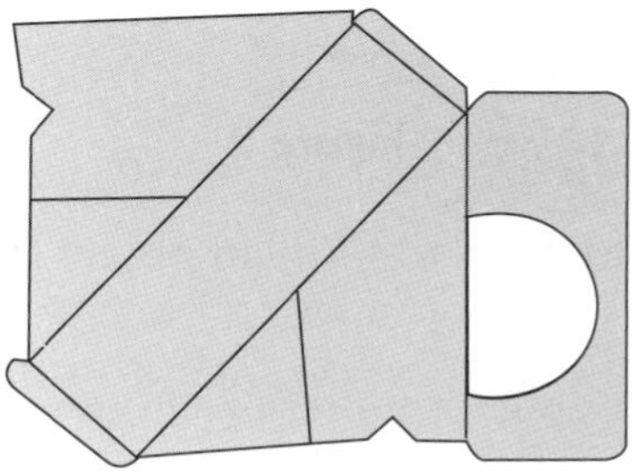

Figure 1

Which **one** of the following CAM machines could be involved in the manufacture of this product?

- **A** CNC router ☐
- **B** Laser cutter ☐
- **C** 3D printer ☐
- **D** CNC milling machine ☐

[1 mark]

3 An engine part is made by the subtraction of material from a solid block.

Which **one** of the following is a suitable CAM machine that could be used to carry out this process?

- **A** 3D printer ☐
- **B** CNC milling machine ☐
- **C** Computer ☐
- **D** Laser cutter ☐

[1 mark]

4 Which **one** of the following CAM machines is suitable for rapid prototyping?

- **A** CNC router ☐
- **B** Laser cutter ☐
- **C** 3D printer ☐
- **D** CNC milling machine ☐

[1 mark]

Section One — Key Ideas in Design and Technology

5   Which **one** of the following statements about CAD is **not** true?

    A   It allows designers to model a product quickly. ☐

    B   CAD software can be used to make 2D or 3D designs. ☐

    C   It allows designers to spot problems with a design before it is made. ☐

    D   It takes a long time to make small alterations to a design made using CAD. ☐

[1 mark]

6   The model shown in **Figure 2** has been made using a 3D printer.

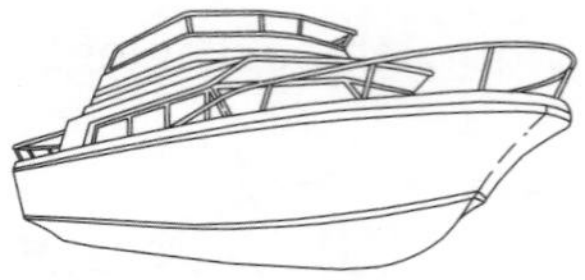

Figure 2

Describe how a 3D printer uses addition to form an object such as the one shown in **Figure 2**.

....

[1 mark]

7   A CNC router is an example of a CAM machine. They can be either 2-axis or 3-axis machines.

    a)   Give **two** ways that a CNC router can be used.

       1.   ....

       2.   ....

[2 marks]

    b)   Explain the difference between 2-axis and 3-axis CAM machines.

       ....

       ....

[2 marks]

8   A UK business sells its products in Europe. It currently designs and manufactures its products in the UK using CAD/CAM. The business is considering moving its manufacturing to Brazil.

Suggest why this relocation of manufacturing might reduce costs for the company.

....

....

[1 mark]

Score: ☐ **/11**

Product Sustainability

Warm-Up

Circle the correct word in each statement below to form correct definitions.

A <u>non-finite</u> / <u>finite</u> resource is one that can be replaced.

A <u>non-finite</u> / <u>finite</u> resource is one that will run out eventually.

1 State **two** factors that influence the sustainability of a product.

1. ....

2. ....

[2 marks]

2 What is meant by planned obsolescence?

....

....

[1 mark]

3 When a new product is made, resources and the final product are transported. This transportation contributes to the product's carbon footprint.

a) Explain why this transportation contributes to the product's carbon footprint.

....

....

[2 marks]

b) Give **two** examples of when transportation that contributes to the product's carbon footprint occurs.

1. ....

....

2. ....

....

[2 marks]

4 The size of a product's carbon footprint has an impact on its sustainability.

a) Why can using an electrical product contribute to its carbon footprint?

....

....

[1 mark]

Section One — Key Ideas in Design and Technology

b) State the link between the size of a product's carbon footprint and its impact on global warming.

....

[1 mark]

5   **Figure 1** shows some paper envelopes and some plastic bubble wrap.

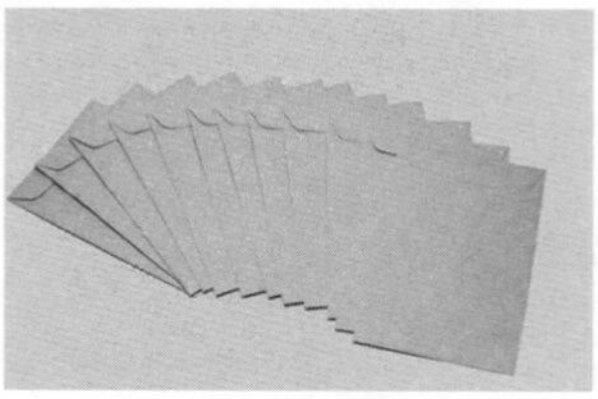

envelopes    bubble wrap

Figure 1

a) The products shown in **Figure 1** are recyclable.
Give **one** reason why this is good for the environment.

....

....

[1 mark]

b) The envelopes shown in **Figure 1** are biodegradable but the bubble wrap is not.
Why does this make the envelopes more sustainable than the bubble wrap?

....

....

[2 marks]

c) A padded envelope is a paper envelope with a layer of bubble wrap inside.
What makes padded envelopes difficult to recycle?

....

....

[2 marks]

6   Products that are designed to be maintained can have less of an impact on the environment
than products which haven't. Explain what is meant by 'design for maintenance'.

....

....

....

[2 marks]

Score: ☐ **/16**

Section One — Key Ideas in Design and Technology

Product Sustainability and Social Issues

Circle the words that make up the 6Rs.

Reallocate   Reduce   React   Remake   Recycle

Rethink   Refuse   Reform   Re-use   Repair

1 Manufacturers are always looking for ways to make their products better. For example, they often change their designs to incorporate new technology. What is this process called?

A   Design for disassembly ☐

B   Continuous improvement ☐

C   Life cycle assessment ☐

D   Product enhancement ☐

[1 mark]

2 Which **one** of the following changes to a product is most likely to be damaging to the environment?

A   Making a product more durable. ☐

B   Changing the design of a product so it can be taken apart for repair. ☐

C   Changing a component in the product to a newer version which gives higher performance but is less reliable. ☐

D   Making the product from materials that are all recyclable. ☐

[1 mark]

3 A power tool company regularly releases new, improved versions of the tools that it manufactures.

a) State **two** reasons why the company regularly releasing new versions of their tools can be environmentally damaging.

1. ....

....

2. ....

....

[2 marks]

b) Explain why newer power tools can have a reduced environmental impact compared to older power tools.

....

....

....

[2 marks]

4 The design, manufacture and disposal of products should have as little impact on the environment as possible.

Choose **one** of the products in **Figure 1**. Explain how its impact on the environment could be limited. Use the ideas of re-use, refuse and reduce.

Disposable plastic razor

Stuffed toy

Figure 1

Product: ....

a) Re-use

....

....

[2 marks]

b) Refuse

....

....

[2 marks]

c) Reduce

....

....

[2 marks]

5 A new design of toothbrush is going to be made from a bioplastic. This plastic is made from plant-based materials.

Explain why using a bioplastic to make toothbrushes is a more environmentally friendly choice of material than using oil-based plastic.

....

....

....

....

[2 marks]

Score: ☐ / **14**

Exam Practice Tip

If you're given a choice of product to answer a question on, it's worth having a <u>quick</u> think about what you could write for each product before you make your decision — don't spend ages deliberating over it though. And make sure you read through the <u>whole question</u> — it'd be no good picking one product and then realising that you can't answer a later question part, but you could have if you'd picked a different product.

Section One — Key Ideas in Design and Technology

 ☐   ☐ ☐

Products in Society

1 Which **one** of the following describes a business that is owned and run by its members?

   A   Co-operative ☐

   B   Enterprise ☐

   C   Virtual market ☐

   D   Partnership ☐

[1 mark]

2 Products can be redesigned in response to market pull.
Which **one** of the following describes market pull?

   A   New technology making a product cheaper to manufacture. ☐

   B   Making a product based on the wants and needs of consumers. ☐

   C   A new material allowing a product to be lighter. ☐

   D   Making a product more expensive to buy. ☐

[1 mark]

3 Businesses and entrepreneurs often come up with new ideas. What is this called?

   A   Enterprise ☐

   B   Reward ☐

   C   Market pull ☐

   D   Innovation ☐

[1 mark]

4 Which **one** of the following does the process of crowdfunding **not** involve?

   A   People called backers that invest in an idea. ☐

   B   Promoting a business idea to try and attract investment. ☐

   C   An application to a bank for a loan. ☐

   D   A website to promote a business idea to potential investors. ☐

[1 mark]

5 A fashion retailer has produced a new range of sportswear.
Suggest how the company could promote the new range using virtual marketing.

....

....

....

[2 marks]

Section One — Key Ideas in Design and Technology

6 The design of a product can be influenced by technology push and market pull.

a) Describe what is meant by technology push.

....

....

[1 mark]

b) An old model and a newer model of smartphone are shown in **Figure 1**.

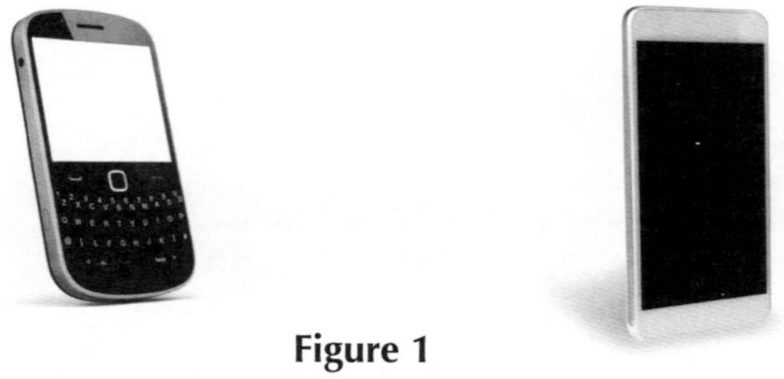

old
model

new
model

Figure 1

i) Identify and explain **one** difference between the smartphones shown in **Figure 1** that could
have been caused by technology push.

....

....

[2 marks]

ii) Identify and explain **one** difference between the smartphones shown in **Figure 1** that could
have been caused by market pull.

....

....

[2 marks]

7 A new mobile phone has been designed to suit the needs of a particular
group of people in society. The phone features large buttons, a high
ringing volume and the ability to make the on-screen text larger.

a) Suggest a group of people in society that this phone may have been designed for.

....

[1 mark]

b) Choose **one** of the features of the new phone and explain how this feature is suited to the needs
of the group of people you've given in part **a)**.

....

....

....

[1 mark]

Score: [   ] / **13**

Section One — Key Ideas in Design and Technology

Powering Systems

Warm-Up Write the resources below in the correct place in the table to show whether they are renewable (non-finite) or non-renewable (finite) energy resources.

coal   solar   tidal

wind   oil   gas

nuclear fuel

hydroelectricity

biomass

Renewable	Non-renewable

1 Describe the difference between renewable and non-renewable energy resources.

....

....

[2 marks]

2 Which **one** of the following statements about power generation from fossil fuels is **not** true?

A   Heat causes water to form steam, which turns turbines. ☐

B   Rotating generators produce electricity. ☐

C   Rotating turbines turn a generator. ☐

D   The flow of water is used to turn a generator. ☐

[1 mark]

3 Which **one** of the following is a feature of alkaline batteries?

A   They can be used more than once. ☐

B   They are built in to products such as mobile phones. ☐

C   Their power output gradually decreases over time. ☐

D   They are expensive. ☐

[1 mark]

4 A company is considering ways to reduce its energy bills. It is considering building either a single wind turbine nearby, or installing solar panels on top of their main factory.

a) Suggest **two** reasons why residents living near the turbine may prefer the use of solar power.

1. ....

2. ....

[2 marks]

b) Suggest **one** reason why the company may choose a wind turbine over solar panels.

....

....

[1 mark]

Section One — Key Ideas in Design and Technology

5   State **two** arguments against the use of fossil fuels as an energy resource.

1. ....

....

2. ....

....

[2 marks]

6   The bar chart in **Figure 1** shows the electricity generated from renewable and non-renewable energy sources in a small country over 20 years.

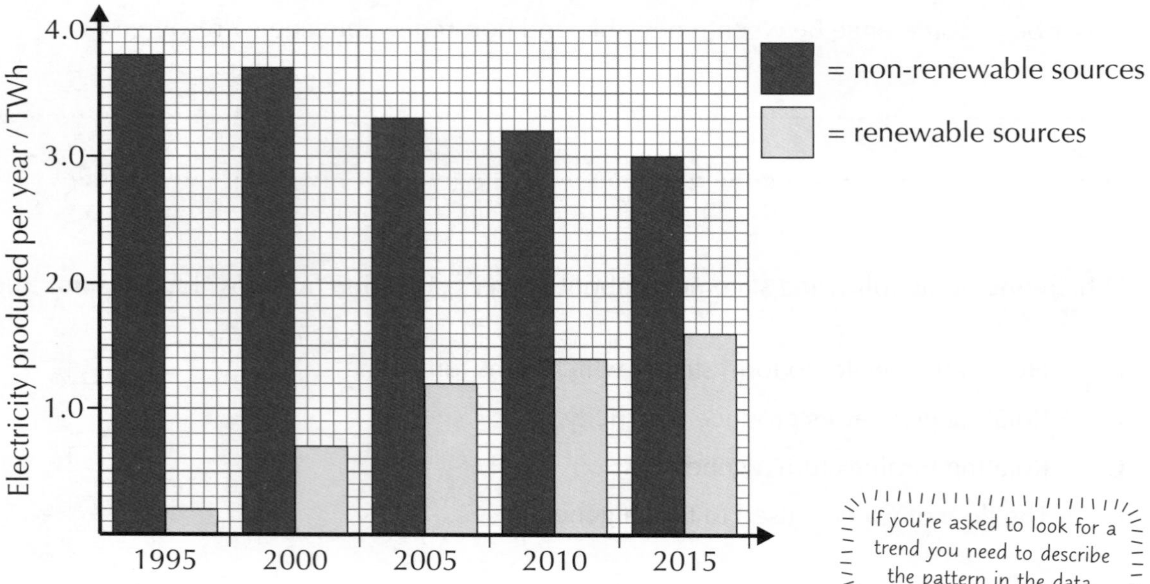

Figure 1

If you're asked to look for a trend you need to describe the pattern in the data.

a)   i)   State the trend in the amount of electricity generated from renewable sources in **Figure 1**.

....

[1 mark]

ii)   Suggest **one** reason for the trend you identified in part **a) i)**.

....

....

[1 mark]

b)   i)   Calculate how much **more** electricity the country produced per year in 2015 than in 1995.

....

....

[2 marks]

ii)   Suggest **one** reason why the country needed to produce more electricity.

....

[1 mark]

Score: ☐ /**14**

Properties of Materials

Warm-Up   Draw lines to match the properties listed on the left with their definitions.

Toughness   The ability to withstand scratching, abrasion or denting.

Hardness   A measure of the mass per unit volume of a material.

Density   The ability of a material to change shape
                     instead of breaking or snapping.

1   Which **one** of the following describes a material's ability to be drawn into a wire?

   A   Malleability   ☐
   B   Fusibility   ☐
   C   Ductility   ☐
   D   Electrical conductivity   ☐

                                                                 [1 mark]

2   Which **one** of the following statements is **not** true?

   A   A spring needs to be elastic so it can return to its original shape
           after being stretched.   ☐
   B   An electrical wire needs to be a good electrical insulator
           so electricity can travel through it easily.   ☐
   C   A towel needs to be absorbent to soak up moisture.   ☐
   D   A climbing rope needs to be strong so that it can hold
           the weight of a person without breaking.   ☐

                                                                 [1 mark]

3   Saucepans are often made of metal. One of the reasons
        for this is that metals are good thermal conductors.

   a)   What is meant by thermal conductivity?

   ....

   ....
                                                                 [1 mark]

   b)   State two other general properties of metals that make them suitable for saucepans.

   1.   ....

   2.   ....
                                                                 [2 marks]

                                                        Score: ☐ /5

Paper, Board and Timber

Warm-Up

Wood can be classified as a hardwood or softwood. Fill in the table below to sort the following types of wood into softwoods and hardwoods.

pine   oak   balsa   beech   larch   spruce   mahogany   ash

Softwood	Hardwood

1   What type of board is made up of expanded polystyrene sandwiched between two thin layers of card?

A   Corrugated cardboard   ☐

B   Solid white board   ☐

C   Duplex board   ☐

D   Foam core board   ☐

[1 mark]

2   A designer wants to make an accurate copy of a design drawing.

Which **one** of the following types of paper would most commonly be used for this purpose?

A   Isometric grid paper   ☐

B   Layout paper   ☐

C   Cartridge paper   ☐

D   Tracing paper   ☐

[1 mark]

3   State **one** property and **one** use for balsa wood.

Property: ....

Use: ....

[2 marks]

4   State **two** properties of oak that make it suitable for use in flooring.

1. ....

2. ....

[2 marks]

Section Two — An Introduction to Materials and Systems

5 Hardwood has some different properties to softwood.

State **two** ways in which the physical or working properties of hardwood and softwood commonly differ.

1. ....

2. ....

[2 marks]

6 Larch is a wood that is often used as cladding to cover the outside of buildings.

Give another use of larch. State a property that makes it suitable for this purpose.

Use: ....

Property: ....

[2 marks]

7 Which **one** of the following statements is **true**?

A Ink jet card is designed to let the ink bleed when used with an ink jet printer. ☐

B Solid white board is bleached white to make it suitable for printing on. ☐

C Isometric grid paper has grid squares printed onto it to make it suitable for orthographic and scale drawings. ☐

D Cartridge paper has a textured surface that can only be drawn on in pencil. ☐

[1 mark]

8 **Figure 1** shows a take-away food box.

Figure 1

a) Suggest a type of board that the box shown in **Figure 1** is made from.

....

[1 mark]

b) Give a reason for your answer to part **a)**.

....

....

[1 mark]

Score: ☐/**13**

Section Two — An Introduction to Materials and Systems

Metals, Alloys and Polymers

1 Which **one** of the following statements about ferrous metals is **not** true?

    A   Ferrous metals are mostly made up of iron. ☐

    B   Ferrous metals are not magnetic. ☐

    C   A protective coating is commonly applied to ferrous metals
to prevent them from rusting. ☐

    D   Tool steel is a ferrous metal. ☐

[1 mark]

2 Which **one** of the following is a type of ferrous metal?

    A   Low carbon steel ☐

    B   Aluminium ☐

    C   Copper ☐

    D   Brass ☐

[1 mark]

3 State **two** properties of copper that make it suitable for use in electrical wiring.

1. ....

2. ....

[2 marks]

4 **Figure 1** shows a brass tap. State **two** properties of brass
that make it a suitable material for this purpose.

1. ....

2. ....

[2 marks]

Figure 1

5 High speed steel is an alloy that can be used to make high speed drill bits.

Explain why high speed steel is a suitable material for this purpose.

....

....

....

[2 marks]

6 Which **one** of the following is a type of thermoforming plastic?

A   Urea-formaldehyde ☐

B   Acrylic ☐

C   Melamine-formaldehyde ☐

D   Polyester resin ☐

[1 mark]

7 Which **one** of the following statements is **not** true?

A   Epoxy resin is rigid and corrosion-resistant. ☐

B   Polyester resin is added to glass fibres to form glass-reinforced plastic. ☐

C   Phenol-formaldehyde is heat-resistant, but hard to mould into different shapes. ☐

D   High impact polystyrene is rigid and used for vacuum forming. ☐

[1 mark]

8 Suggest a plastic that would be suitable for making each of the products shown in **Figures 2-4**. Give **one** reason for each answer.

Figure 2    **Figure 3**    **Figure 4**

a) **Figure 2**

Plastic: ....

Reason: ....

....

[2 marks]

b) **Figure 3**

Plastic: ....

Reason: ....

....

[2 marks]

c) **Figure 4**

Plastic: ....

Reason: ....

....

[2 marks]

Score: ☐ /16

Textiles

1 Which **one** of the following is a type of natural fibre?

    A   Elastane ☐

    B   Cotton ☐

    C   Polyamide ☐

    D   Polyester ☐

[1 mark]

2 Which **one** of the following products is **not** commonly made from silk?

    A   Sportswear ☐

    B   Underwear ☐

    C   Dresses ☐

    D   Ties ☐

[1 mark]

3 **Figure 1** shows a pair of jeans, which are made from a denim.

What type of fibre is used to make denim?

    A   Cotton ☐

    B   Wool ☐

    C   Elastane ☐

    D   Polyester ☐

Figure 1

[1 mark]

4 State **two** ways in which the properties of natural fibres differ to the properties of synthetic fibres.

1. ....

2. ....

[2 marks]

5 Which **one** of the following statements is **not** true?

    A   Yarns are threads that are woven or knitted to make fabrics. ☐

    B   Yarns can be made from staple fibres or filaments. ☐

    C   Staple fibres are shorter in length than filaments. ☐

    D   A 2-ply yarn is made up of two filaments twisted together. ☐

[1 mark]

6 Tights are often made from nylon.

State the type of fibre that nylon is made from.
Give **one** property of nylon that makes it suitable for tights.

Fibre: ....

Property: ....

[2 marks]

7 LYCRA® is a fabric used to make leggings like those in **Figure 2**.

a) Name the fibre used to make LYCRA®.

....

[1 mark]

Figure 2

b) Give **three** properties that you would expect a fabric made from 100% LYCRA® to have.

1. ....

2. ....

3. ....

[3 marks]

c) Apart from leggings, give **one** other use of LYCRA®.

....

[1 mark]

8 Fabric for a school cardigan is to be made from 100% wool.

a) State **two** properties of wool that make it suitable for a cardigan.

1. ....

2. ....

[2 marks]

b) Give **two** reasons why wool might not be the best fibre to use for a school cardigan.

1. ....

2. ....

[2 marks]

Score: ☐ / **17**

Exam Practice Tip

If you get stuck on a question in the exam don't spend ages on it, move on — you can always go back to it if you've got time at the end. It's not worth wasting time on a question you can't answer and missing out on marks that you could pick up in other questions. Just keep your eye on the clock and don't panic if you're unsure of something.

Section Two — An Introduction to Materials and Systems

Textiles and Manufactured Boards

Warm-Up

For each textile product shown below, suggest which type of fabric construction (woven, knitted or non-woven) would most likely have been used.

A: ....

B: ....

C: ....

A   B   C

1   Which **one** of the following types of fabric is made by combining pressure, moisture and heat to interlock a mat of wool fibres?

     A   Mixed fabrics ☐

     B   Felted fabrics ☐

     C   Knitted fabrics ☐

     D   Woven fabrics ☐

                                                                [1 mark]

2   What are bonded fabrics?

     ....

     ....

                                                                [2 marks]

3   A cotton polyester blend is a popular fabric for clothes. State **two** properties of a cotton polyester blend.

     1. ....

     2. ....

                                                                [2 marks]

4   Which **one** of the following statements is **not** true?

     A   A plain weave is made by passing the weft yarn over and under alternate warp yarns. ☐

     B   Woven fabrics are made using a loom. ☐

     C   The warp yarn travels from right to left across the weave, and the weft yarn travels up and down the weave. ☐

     D   The edge of a plain weave, where the weft yarn wraps around the warp yarn, is called the selvedge. ☐

                                                                [1 mark]

5 Which **one** of the following statements about plywood is **not** true?

    A Plywood is made up of several layers of wood that are glued together. ☐

    B The layers of wood are arranged so that the grain direction is the same in each layer. ☐

    C Plywood is strong for its weight and thickness, compared with solid wood. ☐

    D Plywood is often used in building and furniture. ☐

[1 mark]

6 Fibres can be combined by blending or mixing to give fabrics that incorporate the properties of the different fibres used. Explain the difference between a blended fabric and a mixed fabric.

....

....

[2 marks]

7 **Figure 1** is a photo of a manufactured board.

    a) Name the type of manufactured board shown in **Figure 1**.

....

[1 mark]

    b) State **one** product that it could be used in.

Figure 1

....

[1 mark]

8 A charity orders T-shirts made from a plain weave fabric, with its logo printed on them. Give **one** reason why a plain weave fabric is a good choice for the T-shirts.

....

....

[2 marks]

9 **Figure 2** shows a flat-pack cupboard that has been painted white.

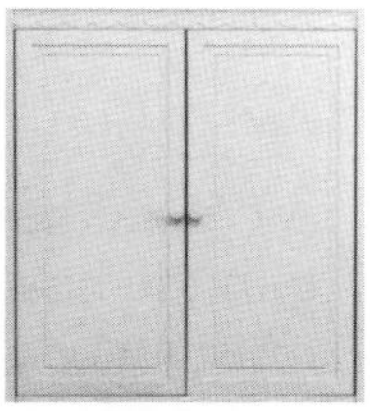

Name a manufactured board that would be suitable for making the flat-pack cupboard shown in **Figure 2**. Give **two** reasons for your answer.

Figure 2

Name: ....

Reasoning: ....

....

....

[3 marks]

Score: ☐/**16**

☹ ☐   😐 ☐   🙂 ☐   **Section Two — An Introduction to Materials and Systems**

Electronic Systems

Warm-Up

Fill in the table to match the names of components with their circuit symbols.

Buzzer
Battery
Switch
Light-dependent resistor (LDR)
Resistor
Thermistor
Bulb

Component	Circuit symbol
	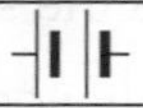
	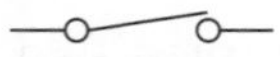
	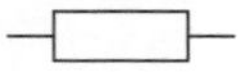
	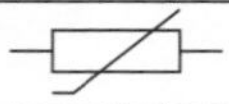
	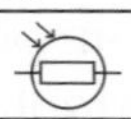
	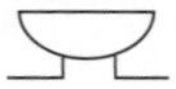
	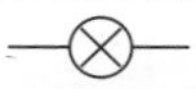

1 A switch can be closed to complete an electronic circuit and allow current to flow. What type of device is a switch?

A Input device ☐
B Process device ☐
C Output device ☐
D None of the above ☐

[1 mark]

2 A washing machine makes a beeping sound when a washing cycle is complete.

a) Name a suitable output device for the system that causes the beeping sound.

....

[1 mark]

b) A light on the washing machine also flashes to show the cycle is complete. Suggest an output device that could be used for this light.

....

[1 mark]

3 A central heating system uses a thermistor to turn the heating off when the thermistor's resistance falls below 10 000 ohms (Ω). This occurs when the room reaches a certain temperature.

Figure 1 shows how the thermistor's resistance changes with temperature. What temperature is the central heating system designed to turn off at?

....

[1 mark]

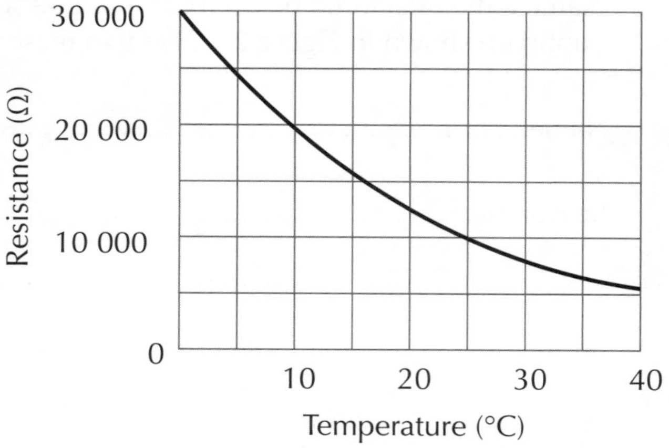

Figure 1

4 Which **one** of the following statements is **not** true?

A   Circuits are made up of components joined together by wires or copper tracks. ☐

B   An electric current pushes a voltage around a circuit. ☐

C   A circuit can be drawn using a circuit diagram. ☐

D   Resistors can be used to reduce the current in a circuit. ☐

[1 mark]

5 What is the definition of a microcontroller?

A   A small remote-controlled system. ☐

B   A timer with memory. ☐

C   A programmable integrated circuit (IC) with a processor and memory. ☐

D   A counter made up of a series of logic gates. ☐

[1 mark]

6 A company is designing a new set of street lights that turn on and off at set times of the day.

a) Explain how a microcontroller could be used to control when the lights turn on and off.

....

....

....

[2 marks]

b) The company found that the lights were turning on too early in the summer, and too late in the winter. They decided to change the street light design so that they turn on when the light levels are below a certain value.

Name a suitable input device for this system. Give a reason for your choice.

Input device: ....

Reason: ....

....

[2 marks]

7 Integrated circuits (ICs) are tiny, self-contained circuits. They can contain billions of components.

Give **two** benefits of using ICs in an electronic system rather than lots of separate components.

1. ....

2. ....

[2 marks]

Section Two — An Introduction to Materials and Systems

8   Which type of logic gate outputs the opposite of the input signal?

    A   OR gates   ☐

    B   AND gates   ☐

    C   NOT gates   ☐

    D   All types of logic gate   ☐

[1 mark]

9   Logic gates are used in systems to make decisions based on a collection of inputs.

    a)   Name the type of logic gate represented in **Figure 2**.

        ....

[1 mark]

Input A	Input B	Output
0	0	0
1	0	1
0	1	1
1	1	1

Figure 2

    b)   Give a reason for your answer to part **a)**.

        ....

        ....

[1 mark]

10   Which **one** of the following is an example of a NOT gate?

    A   An automatic door with an indoor and outdoor sensor.   ☐

    B   An emergency stop switch.   ☐

    C   A machine that's activated only when a key is turned and a switch is pressed.   ☐

    D   An interior light that comes on when one of two car doors are open.   ☐

[1 mark]

11   A designer has constructed a speedometer for a bike. As the front wheel of the bike rotates, a magnet passes a sensor once every turn. This information is passed to a microcontroller and the current speed is shown on an LCD display.

    a)   Name the following devices in this electronic system.

        i)   Input device: ....

        ii)   Output device: ....

[2 marks]

    b)   The microcontroller in this system is used as a counter.
        What does a counter do?

        ....

[1 mark]

Score: ☐ / **19**

> ***Exam Practice Tip***
> Don't be put off if the examiners throw an unfamiliar system at you. It's just a case of applying what you already know about inputs, processes, outputs, etc. — just keep calm and make sure that you read the question carefully.

Mechanical Systems

Warm-Up

Use some of the words in the box to label the diagram of a cam mechanism.

| Cam | Moving pivot | Fixed pivot | Follower | Linkage |

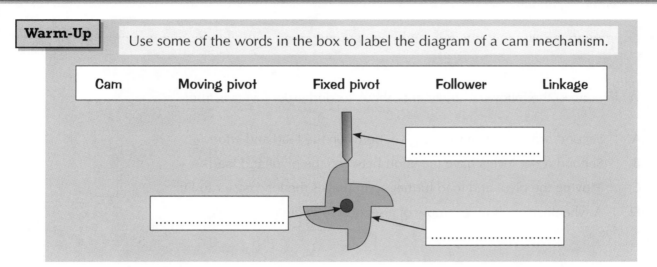

1   **Figure 1** shows a gear train. What is the gear ratio of this mechanism?

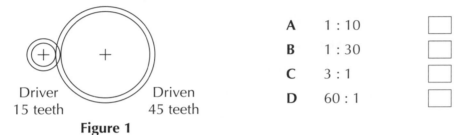

Driver
15 teeth

Driven
45 teeth

Figure 1

A   1 : 10   ☐
B   1 : 30   ☐
C   3 : 1   ☐
D   60 : 1   ☐

[1 mark]

2   **Figure 2** shows a type of linkage.

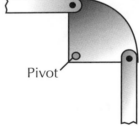
Pivot

Figure 2

a)   Name the mechanism shown in **Figure 2**.

....
[1 mark]

b)   Describe what the mechanism in **Figure 2** does.

....
[1 mark]

3   **Figure 3** shows a crowbar being used to remove a nail from a plank of wood.

Nail   Crowbar
Pivot

Figure 3

a)   A crowbar is an example of a lever. What type of lever is a crowbar?

....
[1 mark]

b) Explain why using this type of lever helps to remove the nail.

....

....

[1 mark]

4 Which **one** of the following statements about second order levers is true?

A Second order levers have the pivot between the load and effort. ☐

B Second order levers have the effort between the pivot and load. ☐

C Moving the pivot and load further apart makes the load easier to lift. ☐

D A wheelbarrow is an example of a second order lever. ☐

[1 mark]

5 Cam mechanisms change one type of motion into another type.
Which **one** of the following describes the change in motion caused by a cam mechanism?

A Rotary motion is converted to linear motion. ☐

B Reciprocating motion is converted to rotary motion. ☐

C Linear motion is converted to oscillating motion. ☐

D Rotary motion is converted to reciprocating motion. ☐

[1 mark]

6 State **two** ways in which a cam could be altered to change the magnitude of the output motion.

1. ....

2. ....

[2 marks]

7 **Figure 4** shows a gear train.

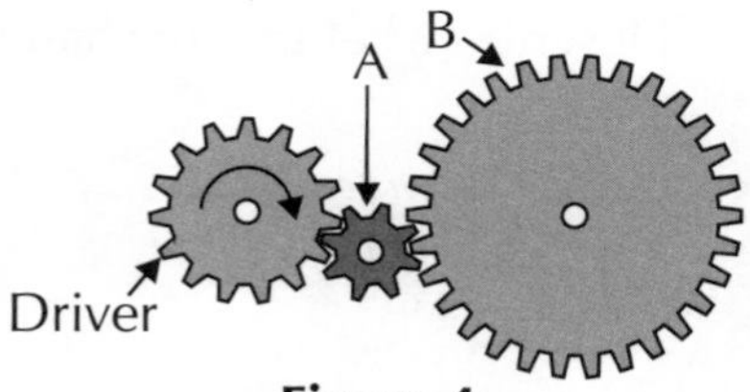

a) Name the gear labelled **A**.

....

[1 mark]

Driver

Figure 4

b) State which direction gear **B** rotates when the driver is turned clockwise. Explain your answer.

....

....

[2 marks]

c) State whether gear **B** will rotate faster, slower or at the same speed as the driver.
Explain your answer.

....

....

[2 marks]

8   The pulley systems A and B shown in **Figure 5** are used to lift a 50 kg load.
Which **one** of the following statements about the pulley systems is true?

A   B

Figure 5

A   The same effort is needed to lift the load with systems A and B. ☐

B   More effort is needed to lift the load with system A than with system B. ☐

C   Both systems A and B give a mechanical advantage. ☐

D   System B requires double the effort to lift the load than system A. ☐

[1 mark]

9   **Figure 6** shows a push/pull linkage. The output force is the same magnitude
and in the same direction as the input force.

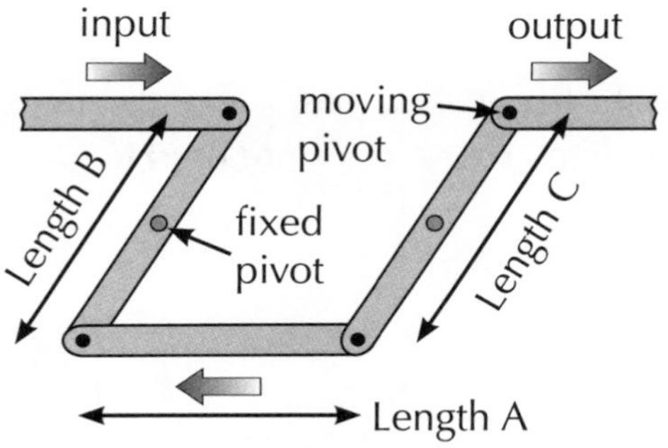

input   output

moving
pivot

Length B

fixed
pivot

Length C

Length A

Figure 6

Which **one** of the following would cause the magnitude of the output force to be different
to the magnitude of the input force?

A   Increasing length A. ☐

B   Increasing the magnitude of the input force. ☐

C   Changing the position of the fixed pivots. ☐

D   Increasing length B and length C by the same amount. ☐

[1 mark]

10 A belt drive mechanism transfers rotary motion
from a motor to a shaft. Details of the mechanism
are given in **Figure 7**.

Part of mechanism	Diameter (mm)
Motor (driver)	35
Shaft (driven)	105

Figure 7

Calculate the velocity ratio for this mechanism.

....

....

[1 mark]

Score: ☐ **/17**

Section Two — An Introduction to Materials and Systems

Developments in New Materials

1   Which **one** of the following is **not** a modern material?

A   Graphene   ☐

B   Liquid Crystal Displays (LCDs)   ☐

C   Brass   ☐

D   Metal foam   ☐

[1 mark]

2   What type of material is titanium?

A   a modern material   ☐

B   a smart material   ☐

C   a composite   ☐

D   a technical textile   ☐

[1 mark]

3   What name is given to materials that change their properties in response to stimuli such as temperature, light, stress, moisture or pH?

A   Technical textiles   ☐

B   Alloys   ☐

C   Modern materials   ☐

D   Smart materials   ☐

[1 mark]

4   Nanomaterials are modern materials.

a)   What are nanomaterials?

....

[1 mark]

b)   Give an example of a nanomaterial and where it is used.

....

....

[2 marks]

5   **Figure 1** shows a pair of sunglasses.

a)   State **one** smart material that could be used to make a part of this product.

....

[1 mark]

Figure 1

b) Explain how the "smart property" of the material you gave in **a)** could be useful to the user of the product.

....

....

....

[2 marks]

6   Which **one** of the following statements is **not** true?

A   Technical textiles are designed to be functional rather than look good.   ☐

B   Kevlar® is a strong synthetic fibre that is resistant to abrasion.   ☐

C   Micro encapsulation allows microfibre fabrics to be embedded with chemicals.   ☐

D   Conductive fabrics use tiny droplets of chemicals coated in shells to conduct electricity.   ☐

[1 mark]

7   Composite materials have useful properties.

a)   What is meant by the term 'composite material'?

....

[1 mark]

b)   Carbonfibre reinforced plastic (CRP) is an example of a composite material. It can be used to make bulletproof vests.

Give **two** properties of CRP that make it a suitable material for this purpose.

1.   ....

2.   ....

[2 marks]

8   An electronics company is designing a warning patch that uses a smart material to show when a microchip begins to overheat.

Suggest and describe a smart material that could be used.

....

....

[2 marks]

Score: ☐ / **15**

Exam Practice Tip

Multiple choice questions can sometimes be hard, but don't panic. The beauty of this type of question is that you can still have a good go at answering it even if you're not sure of the answer — try narrowing down the choices as much as possible, by ruling out which ones are definitely wrong. Then you can pick an answer from one of the options left.

Selecting Materials

Draw circles to show whether the statements below are **true** or **false**.

Designers don't need to compromise when selecting materials — there is always a perfect material for a product or component to be made from.	True / False
Animal products such as fur, ivory and leather are seen as unethical by many people.	True / False
One aesthetic factor to consider when selecting materials is how easy the materials are to work with.	True / False

1   Designers have a social responsibility.

a)   What is meant by the term 'social responsibility'?

....

....

[1 mark]

b)   Suggest why might a company decide to make a design choice that is not socially responsible?

....

....

[1 mark]

2   An outdoors company wants to sell a folding table to be used by campers.

a)   The designers of the table are trying to select a material for the legs and table top.
Give **two** functional considerations that they should bear in mind.

1. ....

....

2. ....

....

[2 marks]

b)   Give **two** aesthetic factors the designers should consider.

1. ....

2. ....

[2 marks]

c) The company wants the table to be manufactured using materials in stock forms and sizes as they are widely available. Give **one** benefit of using widely available materials.

....

....

[1 mark]

d) The company will buy the materials in bulk as they intend to mass produce the table. How might bulk buying the materials affect the price at which the table is sold at? Explain your answer.

....

....

....

[2 marks]

3 A company is designing a bed. They want to limit the impact that the product will have on the environment. One way they can do this is to use ethically sourced materials.

a) What is meant by an ethically sourced material?

....

....

[2 marks]

b) The designer selects timber labelled with the Forest Stewardship Council® (FSC®) logo for the horizontal wooden slats. If timber is labelled with the FSC® logo, what does this mean?

....

....

[1 mark]

c) The bed frame will be made from metal.
The designer is considering using recycled metals or re-used metals.

i) What is the main difference between recycled metal and re-used metal?

....

....

....

[2 marks]

ii) Explain how using recycled or re-used metals to make the bed can help to limit the environmental impact of the product.

....

....

....

[2 marks]

Score: [   ] / **16**

Section Three — More about Materials

Forces and Stresses

1   Different forces are involved in the use of everyday objects.

    a)   **Figure 1** shows a jar. What type of force would be used to twist the lid off the jar?

      ....

                                  [1 mark]

Figure 1

    b)   **Figure 2** shows a pair of secateurs, a scissor-like tool that can be used to cut plants.
        What type of force do the secateurs apply to cut the plants?

      ....

                                  [1 mark]

Figure 2

2   **Figure 3** shows the collar of a shirt that contains interfacings.

    a)   What are fabric interfacings?

      ....

      ....

      ....

                        [1 mark]

Figure 3

    b)   Describe the purpose of interfacings on the collar of the shirt.

      ....

      ....

                                  [2 marks]

    c)   State **one** other part of the shirt that may use interfacings.

      ....

                                    [1 mark]

3   **Figure 4** shows a man in a hammock.

    a)   Force A acts on the ropes that attach the hammock to the beam above. Force B acts on the hammock due to the weight of the man. Name these **two types** of force.

      Force A: ....

      Force B: ....

                         [2 marks]

Figure 4

b) Some hammock straps are made from webbing.

   i) What is webbing?

      ....

      ....

                                                                    [2 marks]

   ii) Suggest why webbing is sometimes used to make hammock straps.

      ....

      ....

                                                                    [1 mark]

4   **Figure 5** shows the structure of corrugated cardboard. It is often used to package heavy loads, because it is strong and rigid.

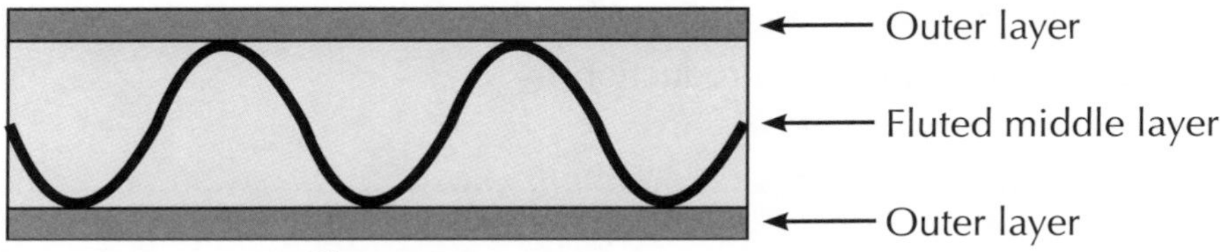

←— Outer layer

←— Fluted middle layer

←— Outer layer

Figure 5

a) Give **two** features of the structure of corrugated cardboard that help to make it strong and rigid.

   1. ....

   ....

   2. ....

   ....

                                                                       [2 marks]

b) Suggest why strength and rigidity are both important for materials that package heavy loads.

   ....

   ....

   ....

   ....

                                                                       [2 marks]

c) Corrugated cardboard packaging is folded along creases to make it easier to form a 3D shape. How is the rigidity at the creases different to the rest of the cardboard?

   ....

                                                                       [1 mark]

Score: ☐ **/16**

Section Three — More about Materials

Scales of Production

1 One-off production is used to make bespoke and custom-made products.

a) Give **one** benefit to the customer of this type of production.

....
[1 mark]

b) Explain why products manufactured by one-off production are likely to be expensive.

....

....
[2 marks]

2 Sheets of glass are usually produced by continuous production.

a) What is meant by the term 'continuous production'?

....

....
[1 mark]

b) Give **one** advantage of using continuous production.

....
[1 mark]

c) Name **one** other product that could be made using continuous production.

....
[1 mark]

3 **Figure 1** shows a one-off designer bag. A manufacturer wants to mass produce a similar bag.

a) Describe the types of product that are most commonly mass produced?

....

....

....
[2 marks]

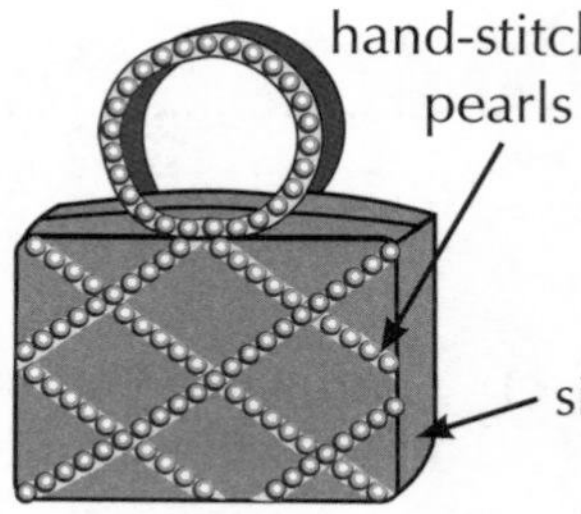

hand-stitched pearls

silk

Figure 1

b) Describe **two** ways in which the bag in **Figure 1** could be adapted for mass production.

1. ....

2. ....
[2 marks]

Section Three — More about Materials

c) Why can mass production be expensive to set up?

....
....
[1 mark]

4 The scale of the production of a product can affect its design.

Choose **one** of the products given below. Suggest how making 1, 300 and 10 000 of the product would affect its design. State the type of production that would be used for each quantity.

| Desk | Formal shoes | Earrings |

Name of product: ....

a) 1 Type of production: ....

How design is affected: ....

....
[3 marks]

b) 300 Type of production: ....

How design is affected: ....

....
[3 marks]

c) 10 000 Type of production: ....

How design is affected: ....

....
[3 marks]

5 State whether one-off, batch, mass or continuous production would be the best method of production in the following situations. Explain your answer in each case.

a) Production of 150 double bed frames and 200 single bed frames.

....

....
[2 marks]

b) Production of a 5-door family car.

....

....
[2 marks]

Score: [ ] **/24**

Quality Control

1   Quality control is an important part of the manufacturing process.

   a) What is the purpose of 'quality control'?

   ....

   ....
   [2 marks]

   b) Explain why only a sample of the manufactured items are used in quality control.

   ....
   [1 mark]

2   **Figure 1** shows a quality control mark used in printing.

   a) Give the name of this mark.

   ....

   [1 mark]

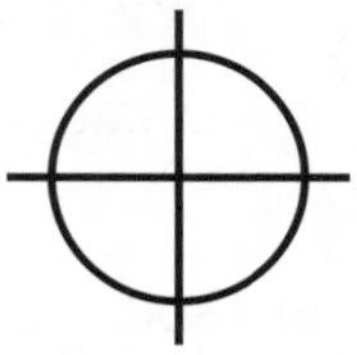

   b) Describe what it is used for.

   Figure 1

   ....

   ....
   [1 mark]

3   **Figure 2** shows a tool used to check that the sizes of components are consistent and within tolerance.

   a) Label **Figure 2** with the dimensions needed to ensure that a component is 50 ± 1 mm thick.

   Upper limit: Lower limit:

   .... mm   .... mm

   Figure 2
   [2 marks]

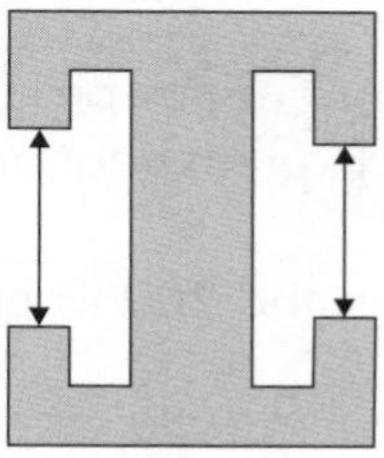

   b) Give the name of this tool.

   ....
   [1 mark]

   c) Give **one** advantage of using this tool instead of a ruler to check the size of components.

   ....

   ....
   [1 mark]

Section Three — More about Materials

4   **Figure 3** shows a design for a ketchup label.

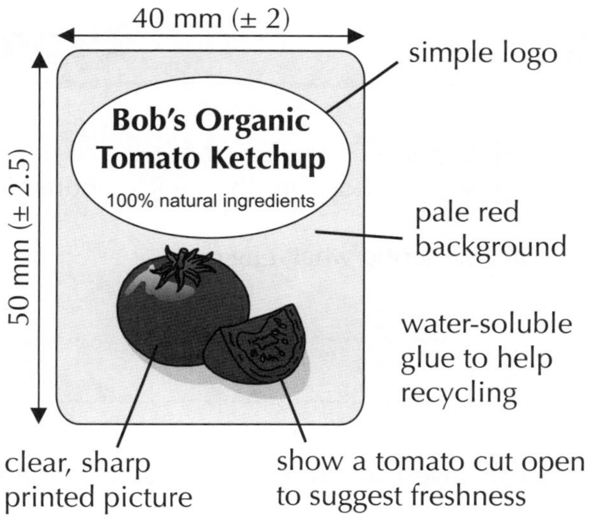

a)   Give **one** quality control check that could be
made on the label.

....

....

....

[1 mark]

b)   The label is going to be stuck onto bottles
at a distance of 25 ± 2 mm from the base.

i)   State the greatest acceptable distance
between the bottom of the bottle and the label.

....

[1 mark]

ii)   Suggest **one** other thing about the label that should be checked after it has been stuck on.

....

[1 mark]

c)   A cut label has a height of 47 mm and a width of 41 mm.
Does the label fall within the stated tolerance? Explain your answer.

....

....

[2 marks]

40 mm (± 2)

50 mm (± 2.5)

simple logo

**Bob's Organic
Tomato Ketchup**

100% natural ingredients

pale red
background

water-soluble
glue to help
recycling

clear, sharp
printed picture

show a tomato cut open
to suggest freshness

Figure 3

5   There are lots of ways of ensuring consistency and accuracy between products during manufacture.

a)   A depth stop can be used to ensure holes are drilled to an exact depth.
Describe how depth stops ensure consistency when drilling.

....

....

[2 marks]

b)   Laser cutters need to have the correct settings selected for the laser to cut out
a material accurately. Give **two** settings which must be correctly selected.

1.   ....

2.   ....

[2 marks]

c)   Photo-etching is a process that is used to manufacture printed circuit boards (PCBs).
Give **one** way of ensuring PCBs are made consistently during photo-etching.

....

[1 mark]

Score: ⬚ / 19

Production Aids

1 A company is producing a batch of shelving units. The shelving units need side panels that have pre-drilled holes for the shelf supports. They have decided to use a drilling jig to make the holes.

a) Describe what a jig does.

....

....

[1 mark]

b) Give **two** advantages of using a drilling jig instead of marking out and drilling the holes by hand.

1. ....

2. ....

[2 marks]

2 **Figure 1** shows a prototype of a birthday card. It's been made by drawing individual balloon and candle shapes by hand, cutting them out and sticking them on top of each other to give a 3D effect.

a) In the space below, sketch a template that could be used to make a batch of 200 of these cards.

Figure 1

[1 mark]

b) State a material that the template could be made from. Explain your choice of material.

....

....

[2 marks]

c) Describe how a template is used.

....

....

[1 mark]

3 Patterns are production aids. They are used in textiles and when casting materials including metals and plastics.

a) Briefly describe how textiles products can be made on a small-scale using patterns.

....

....

....

[3 marks]

b) i) State **one** material that a casting pattern can be made from.

....

[1 mark]

ii) Give **two** benefits of using a pattern to cast a material.

1. ....

2. ....

[2 marks]

4 A company are making a placemat and coaster set. **Figure 2** shows the design for the coaster. The company wants to increase the size of the design by a scale factor of **two** to make the placemat. On **Figure 2**, draw the placemat. Use the datum, i.e. (0,0), as a reference point.

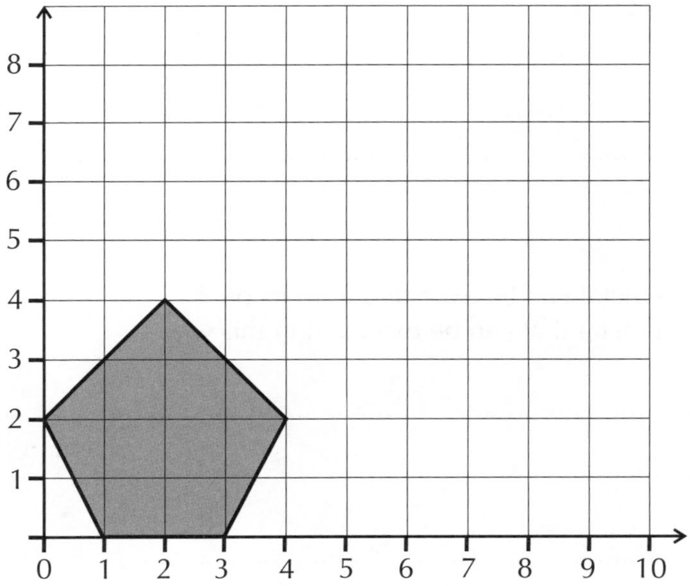

You can use this space to show your working.

....

....

....

....

....

....

....

....

[2 marks]

Figure 2

Score: ☐ /15

Exam Practice Tip

When answering a question that involves a calculation, you should write down any working out that you do. This is important, because even if you get the final answer wrong, you can still pick up some marks if your working is correct.

Production of Materials

1   Plastics are most commonly made from crude oil.

   a)   Give the name of the process where crude oil is separated out into chemicals called fractions.

....
[1 mark]

   b)   Why is 'cracking' sometimes used to manufacture plastics?

....

....
[1 mark]

2   Wood is usually seasoned before it is converted to useful forms.

Give **two** differences between the properties of seasoned and unseasoned wood.

1. ....

2. ....
[2 marks]

3   Metals are extracted from an ore and then refined.

   a)   Describe what is meant by an 'ore'.

....

....
[2 marks]

   b)   What are the **two** main ways in which a metal can be extracted from its ore?
For each process, give **one** example of a metal that can be extracted in this way.

Process: ....

Metal: ....

Process: ....

Metal: ....
[4 marks]

   c)   Explain why metals are refined once they have been extracted from their ore.

....

....
[1 mark]

Section Three — More about Materials

4 Paper and card are made from cellulose fibres, which can come from wood chips.

a) Explain how wood chips can be converted into cellulose fibres.

....

....

....

[2 mark]

b) Describe the process used to convert these fibres to white paper.

....

....

....

[2 marks]

c) Name **one** other raw material that can be used to make paper and board.

....

[1 mark]

5 Wood can be processed into different types of manufactured timbers.

Name the type of manufactured timber shown in **Figure 1**.

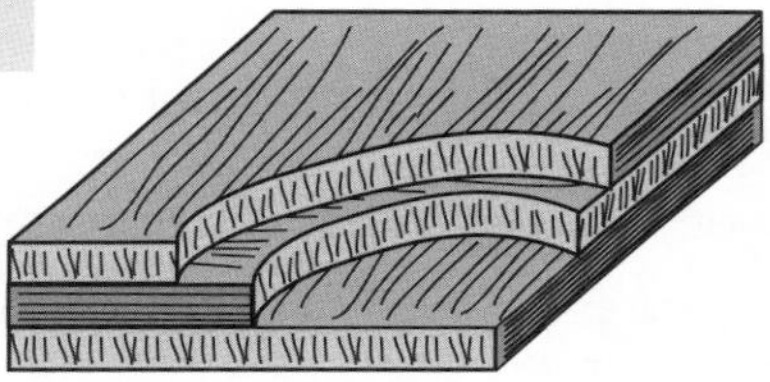

....

Figure 1

Use sketches and/or notes to give a detailed description of the process used to convert wood into this type of manufactured timber.

[5 marks]

Score: [   ] / **21**

More on the Production of Materials

Fibres are made from different raw materials. Draw lines to match the fibres on the left to the raw materials on the right.

Wool   The cocoon of a worm

Silk   Crude oil

Nylon   Sheep's fleece

1 There are three main categories of fibres — natural, regenerated and synthetic.

Give **one** example of a type of fibre from each of these categories.

Natural fibre: ....

Regenerated fibre: ....

Synthetic fibre: ....

[3 marks]

2 Obtaining raw materials can impact the environment.

a) Obtaining timber can cause deforestation.

i) What is deforestation?

....

....

[1 mark]

ii) Explain why deforestation has a negative effect on the environment.

....

....

[2 marks]

b) Give **one** reason why mining has a negative effect on the environment.

....

....

[1 mark]

3 Cotton and polyester fibres are commonly used to make clothes.

a) What are the raw materials used to make cotton and polyester yarns?

Cotton: ....

Polyester: ....

[2 marks]

b) Explain how obtaining these raw materials can negatively impact the environment.
Give **two** ways for each material.

    i) Cotton

       1. ....

       ....

       2. ....

       ....

                                                                                          [2 marks]

    ii) Polyester

       1. ....

       ....

       2. ....

       ....

                                                                                          [2 marks]

c) Choose **one** of these raw materials.
Use sketches and/or notes to give a detailed description of how it is converted to yarn.

    Material: ....

[4 marks]

Score: ☐ / **17**

Exam Practice Tip

If you're asked to describe a process in the exam, it might help to plan your answer first. This can help you to organise your ideas. Jot down the main steps involved in the process and make sure they're in the right order. Then you can pad out your answer, e.g. with a more detailed description, examples, sketches, etc.

  ☺☐

Properties of Paper and Board

Draw circles to show whether the statements below are **true** or **false**.

An A4 sheet of paper is larger than an A0 sheet.   True   /   False

Plain recycled board is good choice of material
for products that need a good finish.   True   /   False

Paper can be sold in rolls.   True   /   False

1   Flyers and leaflets are often printed in low quality.

a)   Why does the print quality not need to be high for flyers and leaflets?

....

[1 mark]

b)   Give one suitable property for the paper used for flyers and leaflets.

....

[1 mark]

2   Paper can be bought in a variety of sizes.

a)   Name the size of paper that matches the following descriptions.

i)   Half the size of A5: ....

[1 mark]

ii)   Double the size of A3: ....

[1 mark]

b)   The area of an A0 sheet of paper is 1 m². Calculate the area of an A3 sheet of paper.

....

....

[1 mark]

3   Name a suitable type of paper or board for each product below,
and state **two** reasons why each material is appropriate.

a)   A soup carton

Type of paper/board: ....

Reason 1: ....

....

Reason 2: ....

....

[3 marks]

b) A takeaway pizza box

Type of paper/board: ....

Reason 1: ....

....

Reason 2: ....

....

[3 marks]

4 During manufacture, additives can be added to paper and board to modify their properties. These additives include treatments that prevent moisture transfer.

a) State **one** example of a type of paper that has been treated to prevent moisture transfer and give **one** application for this type of paper.

....

....

[2 marks]

b) Give **two** other properties of paper and board that can be modified using additives.

1. ....

2. ....

[2 marks]

5 "The best cardboard for packaging products (e.g. boxes) is strong and highly rigid."

Evaluate this statement.

In your answer you should talk about how you agree and disagree with the statement.

....

....

....

....

....

....

....

....

[4 marks]

Score: [   ] **/19**

Section Four — Paper and Board

Standard Components

Circle the standard components shown below that are used with paper and board.

Staples   Tabs   Rivets   Resistors   Drawing pins

Buttons   Plastic comb   Treasury tags   Velcro® pads   Screws

1   A company wants to send out a confidential letter to a client.

    a)   Name a type of envelope that the company could use for the letter. Explain your answer.

      ....

      ....

      [2 marks]

    b)   The company wish to send a large document in the envelope. Name a standard component that could be used to loosely hold the individual pages of the document together.

      ....

      [1 mark]

2   Standard components are pre-manufactured parts.

    Describe the benefits to manufacturers of using standard components in the manufacturing process.

    ....

    ....

    ....

    [2 marks]

3   Bindings can be used to hold sheets of paper together in a book.

    a)   Describe how a book is bound using a perfect binding.

      ....

      ....

      [2 marks]

    b)   Give **one** advantage of using a thread sewn binding over a perfect binding.

      ....

      [1 mark]

    c)   Name a type of binding suitable for a book that will have pages added and removed.

      ....

      [1 mark]

Score: ☐ /9

Working with Paper and Board

Circle the techniques that can be used with paper and/or board.

Creasing   Sawing   Brazing   Scoring   Drilling

Annealing   Cutting   Folding   Perforating   Moulding

1   Paper products can have intricate designs cut into them.
An example is the wedding invite shown in **Figure 1**

These designs can be drawn using computer aided design (CAD) software.
Name a machine that is capable of cutting out such a design,
and describe how it is done.

....

....

[2 marks]

Figure 1

2   **Figure 2** shows a net.

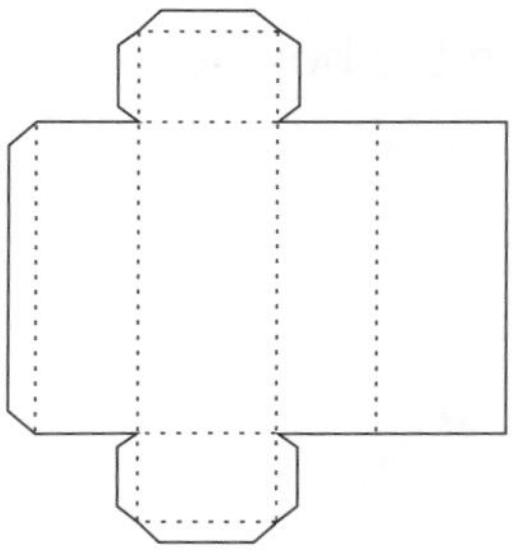

Figure 2

a)   What is a net?

....

....

[1 mark]

b)   i)   Name a machine that could be used to mass produce a net.

....

[1 mark]

ii)   Explain how this machine is used for this purpose.

....

....

....

[2 marks]

iii)   Describe why this machine has high initial set-up costs.

....

....

[1 mark]

c)   One of the dashed lines on **Figure 2** will be perforated. Explain what this means.

....

....

[2 marks]

50

3   **Figure 3** shows a pop-up greetings card made of thin card.
A batch of 20 cards will be made by hand.

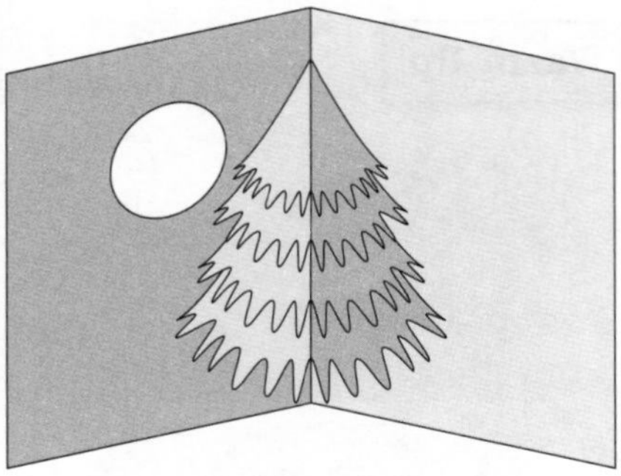

a)   The card has a circular hole in the front.
Suggest a suitable tool for cutting out the circle.

....
[1 mark]

b) i)   The main part of the card is a rectangle folded in half.
Suggest a suitable tool for cutting the rectangle.

Figure 3

....
[1 mark]

ii)   Give **two** advantages of using this tool.

....

....
[2 marks]

c)   The card can be scored to make it easier to fold in half.
Name a cutting tool that can be used to score the card.

Name of cutting tool: ....
[1 mark]

Use sketches and/or notes to give a detailed description of scoring in the box below.
[3 marks]

d)   A scalpel will be used to cut out the fine detail of the pop-up tree.
Give **one** reason why a scalpel is an appropriate tool to use for this purpose.

....
[1 mark]

Score: [   ]/**18**

Section Four — Paper and Board

Printing Techniques

Warm-Up

Draw lines to connect the products on the left with a suitable printing technique on the right.

newspapers   digital printing

flyers   flexography

wallpaper   lithography

1 A design is going to be printed onto a small batch of T-shirts.

a) i) Suggest a printing method that could be used.

....
[1 mark]

ii) Describe the method you named in part **a) i)**.

....

....

....
[2 marks]

b) The T-shirt design is shown in **Figure 1**. Decide whether or not this design is suitable for the method you have chosen and explain your answer.

Figure 1

....

....

....

....
[2 marks]

2 **Figure 2** shows a postage stamp.

a) Stamps are usually made in very large print runs.

i) Name a printing technique that is suitable for printing stamps.

....
[1 mark]

Figure 2

ii) Describe the printing plate that is used in this technique

....
[1 mark]

b) Give a reason why lithography might **not** be suitable for printing stamps.

....
[1 mark]

3   Digital printing uses four process colours (CMYK) and special spot colours.

a)   Explain why some printers use spot colours.

....

....

[1 mark]

b)   Explain why digital printing is cheaper than other printing techniques for short print runs, but not for longer print runs.

....

....

....

....

[2 marks]

4   Offset lithography is a commercial printing technique.

a)   Use sketches and/or notes to explain the technique of offset lithography.

[4 marks]

b)   Flexography is another commercial printing technique.

i)   State a material that printing plates used in flexography can be made from.

....

[1 mark]

ii)   Give **two** reasons why flexography might be used instead of lithography.

1.   ....

2.   ....

[2 marks]

Score: ⬚ / **18**

Section Four — Paper and Board

Paper and Board Finishes

Warm-Up Circle the correct underlined words below, so that each sentence is correct.

Embossing / laminating is the process of sandwiching
a document between two layers of plastic.

Varnish can / can't be written on. Some books are finished by applying a varnish
only to the title — this method of varnishing is known as spot varnishing / flooding.

---

1 Print finishes are applied after a product has been printed.

a) Give **two** advantages of using a print finish.

1. ....

....

2. ....

....

[2 marks]

b) Give **one** disadvantage of using a print finish.

....

[1 mark]

2 Paper products, e.g. menus and posters, can have a laminated finish.

a) Briefly describe the process by which paper is laminated.

....

....

[2 marks]

b) Give **two** reasons why paper products are laminated.

1. ....

2. ....

[2 marks]

3 Varnishing is a type of print finish used by manufacturers.

a) Explain why manufacturers might want to varnish a product.

....

....

[2 marks]

b) Name **one** product that might be varnished. ....

[1 mark]

c) Describe the process of UV varnishing.

....

....

[2 marks]

4 A couple are sending out 100 wedding invitations to their guests. The invitations are to be printed in full colour with foil applied to the names of the couple.

a) i) Describe what is meant by foil application.

....

....

[1 mark]

ii) Suggest **two** reasons why the couple might have chosen to use foil application.

1. ....

2. ....

[2 marks]

iii) The couple are also considering embossing a design onto the invites.
Describe what is meant by embossing.

....

....

[1 mark]

b) The table below shows two quotes for printing the invitations from a local printing company.

i) Complete the table by calculating the price per invitation for each of the quotes.

[1 mark]

	Features of the invitation	Price for 100 invitations	Price per invitation
Quote 1	Full colour + foil application	£180	
Quote 2	Full colour + foil application + embossing	£340	

ii) Calculate the extra cost per invitation of embossing.

....

[1 mark]

iii) Calculate the percentage increase between quote 1 and quote 2.
Give your answer to 1 decimal place.

....

....

[2 marks]

Score: ☐/**20**

Exam Practice Tip

You should know about several different types of finish that can be applied to paper and board — each one protects the product and/or improves its aesthetic. Make sure you remember the differences between them all for the exam.

Section Four — Paper and Board

Uses of Wood, Metals and Polymers

Warm-Up

Circle the correct underlined words below to make each sentence correct.

Annealing involves heating a <u>polymer</u> / <u>metal</u> and leaving it to cool slowly.

This makes it softer, <u>more</u> / <u>less</u> ductile and <u>more</u> / <u>less</u> brittle.

Softening the material makes it more malleable, which makes it <u>easier</u> / <u>harder</u> to bend and shape.

1 A designer is selecting materials to make some products from.
Some of the properties of the materials she is considering are shown in **Figure 1**.

Material	Properties
A	hard, tough, strong, rusts easily
B	doesn't rust easily, high melting point
C	soft, low melting point, corrosion-resistant

Figure 1

a) Using the information in **Figure 1**, give **one** reason why material B is a better choice than material C for making cooking utensils from.

....

....

[1 mark]

b) Give **one** reason why material A is suitable for use as the cutting blade of a bench plane?

....

....

[1 mark]

2 **Figure 2** shows the moisture content of two logs that have been cut from the same tree.

Log	Moisture content (%)
A	49
B	23

Figure 2

a) Which of the logs do you think has been seasoned? Give a reason for your answer.

....

....

[1 mark]

b) Give **two** effects that seasoning has on wood.

1. ....

2. ....

[2 marks]

56

3   **Figure 3** shows a plug socket.
     It is made from a thermosetting plastic.

Figure 3

a)   Suggest which thermosetting plastic the plug
     socket in **Figure 3** could be made from.

     ....
                                                    [1 mark]

b)   Give **two** properties of the plastic you choose in part **a)** that makes it suitable for use
     in electrical fittings. Explain why these properties make it a suitable choice.

     1. ....

     ....

     2. ....

     ....
                                                    [4 marks]

4   A company is designing seating for use in an outdoor football stadium.
     They decide to make the seats out of the thermoforming plastic polypropylene.

a)   State **two** properties of polypropylene that make it a suitable material
     for outdoor stadium seating. Give a reason for each property stated.

     1. ....

     ....

     2. ....

     ....
                                                    [4 marks]

b)   A chemical called a stabiliser is added to the polypropylene during production.
     Explain why this is done.

     ....

     ....

     ....

     ....

     ....

     ....

     ....
                                                    [4 marks]

Score: ☐ /18

Section Five — Wood, Metals and Polymers

Stock Forms and Standard Components

1 Metals can be supplied in different shapes and sizes.

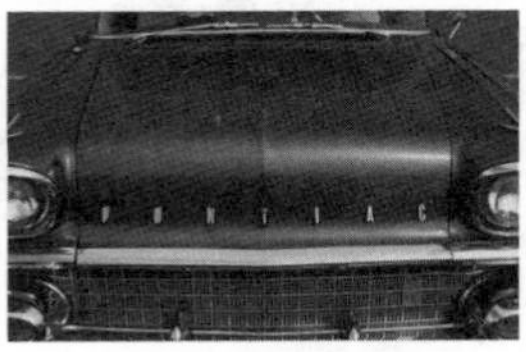

Figure 1

Suggest what shape of metal a manufacturer would use to make the following products:

a) the car bonnet shown in **Figure 1**.

....
[1 mark]

b) the bicycle frame shown in **Figure 2**.

....
[1 mark]

Figure 2

c) Explain why metals being available in a wide range of shapes and sizes is useful for manufacturers.

....

....
[2 marks]

2 **Figure 3** shows a simple wooden picture frame made from 4 lengths of timber.

a) The planed square edge timber used to make the frame comes in standard lengths of 1 m. How many would be needed to make one frame?

....

....

....
[2 marks]

Figure 3

b) Strips of timber are available in a range of cross sections as shown in **Figure 4**.

i) What are the strips of timber in **Figure 4** known as?

....
[1 mark]

ii) These strips of timber can be used to make the frame shown in **Figure 3**. Give **one** other use for these strips of timber.

....
[1 mark]

Figure 4

c) A back panel for the picture frame is to be made from MDF. What form are manufactured boards such as MDF usually bought in?

....
[1 mark]

Section Five — Wood, Metals and Polymers

3   Polymers are available in many different forms.

a)   Suggest which form of polymer could be used to produce each of the following products.

i)   The window in the sandwich box shown in **Figure 5**.

....
[1 mark]

ii)   The protective packaging inside the box a TV is sold in.

....
[1 mark]

Figure 5

Cheese Supreme

b)   Give **one** form of polymer that can be used for moulding.

....
[1 mark]

c)   A design for a product includes some polymer sheet that is at least 1.5 mm thick. The manufacturer has some polymer sheet in stock that is 1800 μm thick. Is this sheet suitable for use in the product? You must show your working. (1 mm = 1000 μm)

....

....
[2 marks]

4   Screws and bolts are standard components used to join different materials together.

a)   Some screws are self-drilling. Explain what this means.

....

....
[1 mark]

b)   What type of materials are nuts and bolts used to join?

....
[1 mark]

c)   Sketch a bolt in the box below. Include labels for the shank and thread.

[2 marks]

d)   Name a hand tool that is used to tighten bolts.

....
[1 mark]

Score: ☐ /19

More Standard Components

1   A company is designing a flat-pack wardrobe.
A prototype of the wardrobe is shown in **Figure 1**.

Figure 1

a)   Hinges will be needed to allow the doors
of the wardrobe to open.

i)   Name **one** type of hinge that would be suitable
for this purpose.

....
[1 mark]

ii)   State **two** materials that the hinges could be made from.

1.   ....

2.   ....
[2 marks]

b)   The rest of the wardrobe will be held together using knock-down (KD) fittings.

i)   Explain why KD fittings are suitable for this flat-pack product.

....

....

....
[2 marks]

ii)   Name a KD fitting that would be suitable for holding the shelves in position.

....
[1 mark]

2   A rivet can be used to permanently join sheets of metal.

Use sketches and/or notes to explain how a rivet can be used for this purpose.

[4 marks]

Score: [   ] / **10**

Shaping Materials — Hand Tools

1 A bed and breakfast owner wants to make a door knob hanger for each of the guest bedrooms. The hangers will be made from thin acrylic. The design for the hanger is shown in **Figure 1**.

a) Suggest a hand tool that could be used to cut the outline of the hanger. Give a reason for your answer.

Hand tool: ....

Reason: ....

....

[2 marks]

b) Suggest a type of drill bit that could be used to make the hole in the hanger.

....

[1 mark]

hole for door hanging

Please Do Not Disturb

Figure 1

2 A carpenter is making an oak key rack, shown in **Figure 2**.

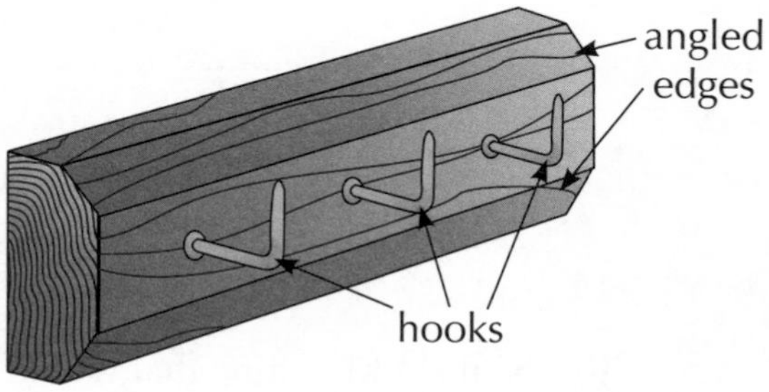

a) State a type of saw that could be used to cut the length of oak to the right size.

....

[1 mark]

angled edges

hooks

Figure 2

b) Once sawn, the ends of the key rack are sanded with abrasive paper to smooth them down. Give **one** benefit of using a sanding block when sanding.

....

....

[1 mark]

c) The carpenter presses a bradawl into the wood where a hole is to be made for each hook. Explain why the carpenter does this before the holes are drilled.

....

....

[2 marks]

d) Name a hand tool that could be used to produce the angled edges of the front of the key rack.

....

[1 mark]

Score: ☐ /8

Section Five — Wood, Metals and Polymers

Shaping Materials — Power and Machine Tools

Using the words given below, name the tools shown in the photos.

pillar drill   router

band saw   planer

saw bench

A: ....   B: ....

---

1   A band saw and a saw bench are types of machine tools used to cut materials.

State **two** of the main differences between a band saw and a saw bench.

1. ....

....

2. ....

....

[2 marks]

---

2   George is making a cut out of a tree for some stage scenery.
He has drawn the shape of the tree onto a piece of plywood.

Name a power tool that could be used to cut out the tree shape from plywood.
Give a reason for your answer.

....

....

[2 marks]

---

3   Power tools are hand-held and motorised.

a)   Give **three** safety precautions that need to be taken when working with power tools.

1. ....

2. ....

3. ....

[3 marks]

b)   Machine tools generally do the same jobs as power tools, but are not hand-held.
Give **one** advantage of machine tools compared to power tools.

....

[1 mark]

4　A carpenter is making a wooden desk with drawers and a rectangular top.

    a)　**i)**　The carpenter wants to cut grooves into the front of the drawers to make them look more attractive. Name a power tool that could be used to cut these grooves.

            ....

                                                                                                        [1 mark]

        ii)　How could the carpenter make sure the grooves are cut parallel to the edge of the drawer front?

            ....

                                                                                                        [1 mark]

    b)　Woodscrews will be used to assemble the drawers.
Name a machine tool that could be used to drill pilot holes in the different parts of the drawer.

            ....

                                                                                          [1 mark]

    c)　The sheet of wood used for the desktop is 3 mm thicker than the thickness specified in the design. Name a power tool that could be used to reduce its thickness.

            ....

                                                                                          [1 mark]

5　A sanding disc is an example of a machine tool that can be used with wood.

    a)　Describe how a sanding disc works.

            ....

            ....

                                                                                        [1 mark]

    b)　How would a sanding disc being used with metals differ from one being used with wood?

            ....

                                                                                          [1 mark]

    c)　Sanding discs can produce a lot of dust when machining, which can be unsafe if breathed in.
What can be attached to the machine to reduce the amount of dust released into the air?

            ....

                                                                                          [1 mark]

Score: ☐ **/15**

Exam Practice Tip

When learning about hand and power tools it's important to think about what they might be used for. This will help you out when you're asked about which tools are suitable for a particular job. Look at some different products around you and think about what tools could be used to make them — if you're not sure, do some research online.

Section Five — Wood, Metals and Polymers

Shaping Techniques

Warm-Up

Draw circles to show whether the statements below are **true** or **false**.

Sheets of aluminium can be bent using a sheet metal folder.   True / False

Milling machines add thin layers to a material, one at a time.   True / False

1   The book end shown in **Figure 1** is made using acrylic.

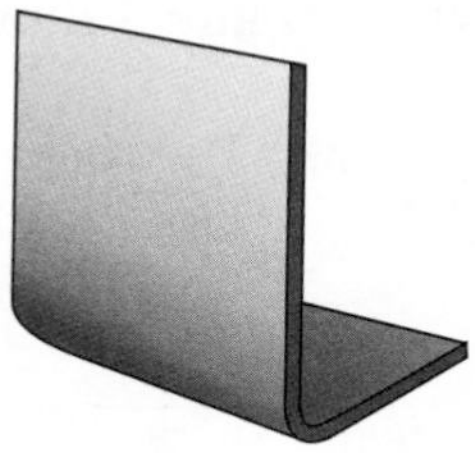

   a)   Suggest **one** piece of equipment that could be used to bend the acrylic.

   ....

   [1 mark]

Figure 1

   b)   Describe the process used to bend the acrylic.

   ....

   ....

   ....

   [3 marks]

2   The body of the model car shown in **Figure 2** is made of metal, and has been produced using die casting.

   Use sketches and/or notes to give a detailed description of the die casting process for this product.

Figure 2

[4 marks]

Section Five — Wood, Metals and Polymers

64

3   3D printing is an additive CAM process. Describe how 3D printing
     can be used to turn a design idea into a finished 3D model.

     ....
     ....
     ....
                                                                                       [2 marks]

4   **Figure 3** shows a design for a wooden rocking chair.

     a)   The rockers are made from strips of laminated wood.
          Use sketches and/or notes to give a detailed description of
          how lamination could be used to make the rockers.

Figure 3

                                                                                       [4 marks]

     b)   **Figure 4** shows a close-up of the vertical supports on the back of the chair.
          These are called spindles.

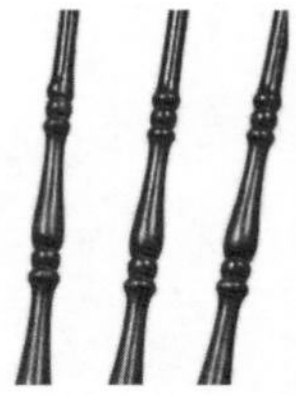

          i)   Suggest a piece of equipment that could be used
               to shape these spindles.

               ....
                                                                    [1 mark]   **Figure 4**

          ii) Describe how the piece of equipment named in part **i)** can be used to shape the spindles.

               ....
               ....
               ....
               ....
                                                                                       [2 marks]

                                                                   Score: [   ]/**17**

Moulding and Joining

1 Glue is used to bond materials together. For example, joints can be secured or reinforced with glue.

a) Give **one** example of a type of glue that could be used to bond pieces of card together.

....
[1 mark]

b) Give **one** advantage and **one** disadvantage of using superglue to bond materials.

Advantage: ....

Disadvantage: ....
[2 marks]

2 **Figure 1** shows a plastic box that is made using injection moulding.

Use sketches and/or notes to explain the process of injection moulding.

Figure 1

[4 marks]

3 Soldering, brazing and welding are three methods of joining metals together.

a) Describe the process of soldering. Give the name of any tools used in the process.

....

....
[2 marks]

b) i) Brazing is a higher temperature process than soldering.
State a joining material that can be used in the brazing process.

....
[1 mark]

ii) Give **one** advantage of using brazing to join metals instead of soldering.

....
[1 mark]

Section Five — Wood, Metals and Polymers

c) Welding is also a high temperature process.
Describe the process by which polymers are welded together.

....

....

....

....

[3 marks]

4   The products shown in **Figure 2** are all made using a mould.

Choose **one** product in **Figure 2** and name the moulding process that is used to manufacture it.
Use sketches and/or notes to give a detailed description of the moulding process of this product.

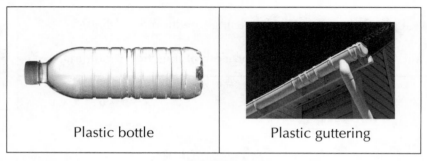

| Plastic bottle | Plastic guttering |

Figure 2

Name of product/component: ....

Moulding process: ....

> If you want some extra practice, use a spare piece of paper to write down an answer for the other product too.

[5 marks]

Exam Practice Tip

There's likely to be at least one question in the exam where you're given a choice of materials or products to pick from.
It's worth taking time to read the whole question, so you can figure out which option you can write the best answer for.

5   A design for a curved, plastic lamp shade is shown in **Figure 3**.
     The shade is made of a single sheet of plastic.

Figure 3

a)   Name a method that could be used to form the lamp shade shown in **Figure 3**.

Method: ....
                                                                                                              [1 mark]

b)   Use sketches and/or notes to give a detailed description of how the method you named in
     part **a)** could be used to form the lamp shade in **Figure 3**.

                                                                                                              [3 marks]

c)   Decoration is to be added to the lamp shade to make the design less plain.
     The designer plans to do this by attaching small pieces of plastic to the outside of the shade.

     Suggest how these decorative shapes could be attached to the lamp shade
     without the need to use high temperatures.

     ....

     ....
                                                                                                              [1 mark]

Score: [   ] **/24**

 [   ]   [   ]   ☺ [   ]

Section Five — Wood, Metals and Polymers

Treatments and Finishes

1   Steel can be coated with zinc to stop it from rusting.
    For example, car bodies are often made from a zinc-coated steel.

a) What causes steel to rust?

    ....
    [1 mark]

b) Name the process in which steel is coated with zinc.

    ....
    [1 mark]

c) Explain how the zinc layer prevents the steel from rusting.

    ....
    ....
    ....
    [2 marks]

2   The oak dining table shown in **Figure 1** has been finished with a varnish.

a) Describe one way in which the oak could have been prepared before varnishing.

    ....
    ....
    ....
    [2 marks]

Figure 1

b) Suggest why varnish has been chosen rather than paint to coat the surface of the table.

    ....
    ....
    [1 mark]

c) The table needs a finish that protects it from knocks and scratches.
    Suggest a suitable type of varnish that could be used, and give a reason for your answer.

    ....
    ....
    [2 marks]

3   **Figure 2** shows a garden bench that is to be finished with paint.

a) One reason for painting the bench is to protect it from decay.
    Give **one** other reason for painting the bench.

    ....
    [1 mark]

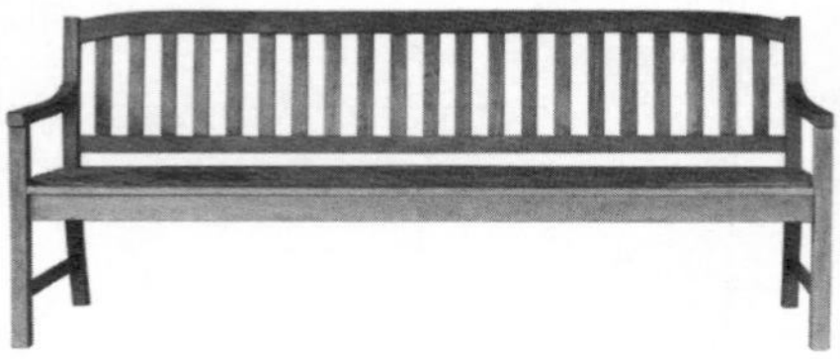

Figure 2

b) The bench needs to be primed before painting.
State **two** ways in which a primer helps to prepare the wood for painting.

1. ....

2. ....
[2 marks]

c) Name the type of paint used on top of a coat of primer?

....
[1 mark]

d) Suggest why it is a good idea to construct the bench using tanalised® wood, even though the paint finish will protect it from insect attacks and decay.

....

....
[1 mark]

4 Powder coatings can be used as a finish for products such as wheels and bicycle frames.

a) Describe how metals should be prepared before they are powder coated.

....

....

....
[2 marks]

b) Use sketches and/or notes to explain the method of powder coating metal objects.

[4 marks]

c) Give **one** advantage of powder coating.

....
[1 mark]

Score: ☐ / **21**

Section Five — Wood, Metals and Polymers

Fabrics and Their Properties

Warm-Up

Circle properties that can be added to a fabric through the use of chemical treatments.

Stain protection

Flame retardance

Water resistance

Electrical conductivity

Malleability

1   Acrylic fibres are often used in furnishings such as carpets.

Give **two** properties of acrylic fibres that make them suitable for use in carpets.

1. ....

2. ....

[2 marks]

2   Chemical treatments are applied to fabrics during the manufacturing process.

Name **one** treatment that is suitable for use with each of the following products.
Give a reason for each choice.

a)   A nylon coat.

Treatment: ....

Reason: ....

[2 marks]

b)   Carpet in a dining room.

Treatment: ....

Reason: ....

[2 marks]

3   A sports T-shirt is to be made from 100% polyester.

Give **two** properties of polyester and explain why each one makes it appropriate for sports use.

1. ....

....

2. ....

....

[4 marks]

4   Flame retardant treatments can be applied to clothes such as overalls used by welders.

a) What is the function of a flame retardant treatment?

....

[1 mark]

b) Why is flame retardance an important property for welder's overalls?

....

....

[1 mark]

c) Name **one** other type of clothing that might have been given a flame retardant treatment.

....

[1 mark]

d) Give **one** disadvantage of using a flame retardant treatment.

....

[1 mark]

5   A company are designing a new waterproof coat. The design contains a delicate, waterproof membrane between two other layers of fabric.

a) Name the process used to construct a fabric that contains two or more layers.

....

[1 mark]

b) The waterproof membrane allows sweat to escape without letting rain in.
Explain the function of the layers of fabric that this membrane is placed between.

....

....

[2 marks]

c) In cheaper products the company uses a water resistant finish to coat fabrics.
Why does this finish not provide full waterproofing?

....

....

[1 mark]

Score: [ ] /**18**

Exam Practice Tip

You should read a question thoroughly **before** you start to write an answer. Look out for the command word (or words) being used, e.g. name, describe, explain, etc. This will give you an idea of how to answer the question. For example, you don't need to give an explanation to a question that uses 'give' — you'll just be wasting precious time in the exam...

Section Six — Textiles

Standard Components and Tools

1 An iron can be used to press creases out of a fabric.

Give **two** other ways that an iron can be used when making textile products.

1. ....

2. ....

[2 marks]

2 Textiles products can be made using a wide variety of tools.

a) Name **two** tools that can be used in the process of marking out patterns.

1. ....

2. ....

[2 marks]

b) i) Describe the main difference between dressmaking and embroidery scissors.

....

....

[1 mark]

ii) Describe how these types of scissors are used differently.

....

....

[2 marks]

c) Why are seam rippers better suited to unpicking seams than scissors.

....

....

[1 mark]

3 Velcro® is to be used as a fastening for the child's apron shown in **Figure 1**.

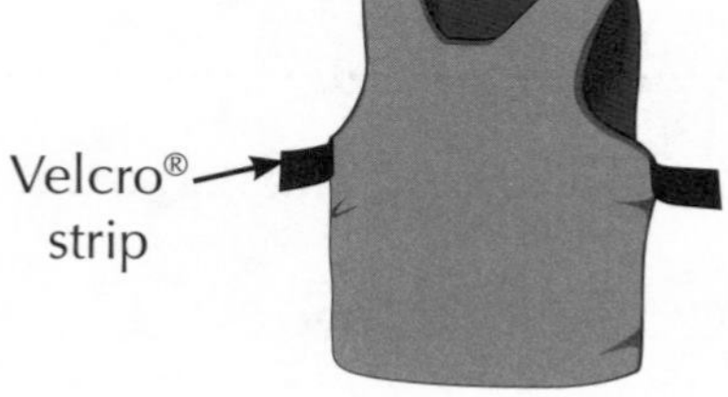

Velcro®
strip

Figure 1

a) Describe briefly how Velcro® works as a fastening.

....

....

[1 mark]

b) Evaluate the use of Velcro® to fasten the apron shown in **Figure 1**.

....

....

....

....

....

....

[4 marks]

4 A seamstress is buying materials to make a shirt. Three different fabrics that could be used for the shirt are shown in the table below.

Fabric	Width (cm)	Cost per metre (£)	Length needed (m)	Total cost of fabric (£)
A	132	5.50	1.70	
B	150	7.40	1.55	
C	150	6.20	1.55	9.61

a) Complete the table by calculating the total cost for fabrics A and B.

....

....

....

[1 mark]

b) i) The seamstress decides to use **fabric C**. However, a change is made to the design of the shirt, which means the length of material needed increases to 1.90 metres.
Calculate the new total cost of fabric required to make the revised design.

....

[1 mark]

ii) Calculate how much more of fabric C is required for the revised design compared to the original design. Your answer should be given in m² and to two decimal points.

....

....

....

[3 marks]

c) The seamstress has chosen to use press studs to fasten the shirt.
Suggest **one** user benefit of the shirt having press studs rather than buttons.

....

[1 mark]

Score: ☐ /**19**

Section Six — Textiles

Joining and Shaping Fabrics

Warm-Up Draw circles to show whether the statements below are **true** or **false**.

Sewing is used to join fabrics temporarily.   True / False

Overlockers are used to finish edges to stop them from fraying.   True / False

Gathering involves stuffing wadding between two layers of fabric.   True / False

1 A rugby shirt is to be made with plain (flat) seams.

a) What is the purpose of a seam?

....

[1 mark]

b) Use notes and diagrams to explain how to make a plain seam.
Include information about the materials and equipment needed.

[4 marks]

c) Why might using plain seams not be a good choice for a rugby shirt?

....

....

[2 marks]

d) Name the type of seam that would be appropriate to use when making the following clothes.
Explain your answers.

i) Baby's dress: ....

....

....

ii) Corduroy trousers: ....

....

....

[4 marks]

2 The pieces of fabric for a T-shirt have been cut out.
The next step is to stitch the seams and neaten the edges.

Explain why it would be more efficient to use an overlocker
rather than a sewing machine for this task.

....

....

....

[2 marks]

3 **Figure 1** shows a coat that has been quilted.

a) Describe what is meant by quilting.

....

....

....

[2 marks]

b) Give **one** function of the quilting in this coat.

....

[1 mark]

Figure 1

4 Fabrics can be stitched together by hand or using a sewing machine.

a) **i)** When are sewing machines better suited to stitching fabrics than hand-sewing?
Give a reason for your answer.

....

....

[2 marks]

ii) Explain when hand-sewing is more suitable for stitching fabrics than a sewing machine.

....

....

[2 marks]

b) A sewing machine is being prepared for use. The machine is used to sew a line of stitches in a
spare piece of fabric. Suggest why this is done.

....

....

[1 mark]

Section Six — Textiles

5 Piping adds definition to a seam. It is used in products such as sofa cushions.

a) Use notes and/or sketches to explain how piping is constructed and added to a seam.

[3 marks]

b) Give **two** reasons why piping might be added to a textiles product.

1. ....

2. ....

[2 marks]

6 Pinning and tacking are two ways in which fabrics can be temporarily joined together.

a) Why are fabrics pinned and/or tacked before they are sewn together?

....

[1 mark]

b) Use sketches and/or notes to explain the process of pinning and tacking two fabrics together. Include information about the materials and equipment needed.

[3 marks]

c) Some fabrics can be damaged by pinholes or tacking stitches.
Suggest an alternative way of joining these fabrics together temporarily.

....
[1 mark]

7 Computer technology can be used in the design and manufacture of clothes.

a) Describe how computer technology can be used to add embroidery to a T-shirt.

....

....
[2 marks]

b) Suggest **one** advantage of using the computer technology described in **a)** over hand embroidery.

....

....
[1 mark]

8 A designer wants to add shape to a skirt by making it tighter at the waist and fuller at the hips.

a) One way of achieving this is by adding pleats.
Use sketches and/or notes to explain the process of pleating.

[4 marks]

b) Name and describe another shaping technique the designer
could use to tighten the skirt at the waist.

Name: ....

Description: ....

....

....
[4 marks]

Score: ⬜ /**42**

Section Six — Textiles

Dyeing

1 Dyes come under two main categories — natural dyes and chemical dyes.

a) What are dyes used for in the textiles industry?

....
[1 mark]

b) Give **one** example of a natural dye.

....
[1 mark]

c) Chemical dyes are brighter and cheaper than natural dyes. Give **one** reason why a designer may still choose to use a natural dye rather than a chemical one.

....
[1 mark]

2 Fabrics can be dyed using either commercial or hand dyeing methods.

a) Give **one** advantage of commercial dyeing over hand dyeing.

....
[1 mark]

b) Give **one** advantage of hand dyeing over commercial dyeing.

....
[1 mark]

3 Dyes often need to be fixed to the fabric once they have been applied. This often involves oxidising the dye.

Explain the role of oxidation in the fixing process.

....

....

....
[2 marks]

4 Some fabrics can be dyed more easily than others.

a) Give **one** example of a fabric that is good for dyeing, and explain your answer.

....
[2 marks]

b) Why do some fabrics need to be bleached before dyeing?

....
[1 mark]

Section Six — Textiles

5 Batch dyeing is a process that is often used in the textiles industry.

a) Describe how this process works.

....

....

....
[3 marks]

b) Give **one** benefit of using batch dyeing in industry.

....
[1 mark]

6 Resists can be used when hand dyeing to create patterns on the fabric.

a) Describe how a resist is used in the process of hand dyeing.

....

....
[1 mark]

b) i) **Figure 1** shows a design created by hand dyeing. Name a hand dyeing method that could be used to create these patterns.

....
[1 mark]

ii) Briefly describe the main steps in this method.

....

....

Figure 1

....

....
[3 marks]

c) i) Name **one** other method of hand dyeing, and describe what is used as a resist in this method.

....

....
[2 marks]

ii) State **two** disadvantages of the method named in part **c) i)**.

1. ....

2. ....
[1 mark]

Score: ☐/**22**

Section Six — Textiles

Printing

1   Give **two** substances, other than inks, that can be used to produce a printed design on fabric.

1. ....

2. ....

[2 marks]

2   Screen printing can be done by machine or by hand.

a)   Name **two** pieces of equipment that both machine and hand screen printing methods use.

1. ....

2. ....

[2 marks]

b)   Using sketches and/or notes, explain how flat-bed screen printing can be done by hand.

[4 marks]

c)   Describe **two** ways in which the method explained in part **b)** is modified to be carried out by machines.

1. ....

2. ....

[2 marks]

d)   Rotary-screen printing is another screen printing method. It is operated using machines.

State the main advantage of using rotary screen printing instead of industrial flat-bed screen printing.

....

[1 mark]

3 A batch of 40 T-shirts are to have a simple repeating star design like the one shown in **Figure 1**.
The stars are to be printed in different colours, and they are to be printed using a block printing method.

Figure 1

a) Using sketches and/or notes, explain how block printing can be used to make this T-shirt.

[3 marks]

b) Suggest **two** advantages of using block printing for this batch of T-shirts.

1. ....

2. ....

[2 marks]

c) A different batch of T-shirts uses a more detailed design which isn't suitable for block printing. Suggest an appropriate alternative printing method.

....

[1 mark]

Score: ☐ /**18**

Exam Practice Tip

If you want to draw a sketch or diagram, make sure you add annotations (notes) — they can be used to label different parts of a diagram and explain what a diagram is trying to show. Sometimes it's easier to draw something than explain it just using words, but it's a good idea to annotate it too so the person marking your answer knows what you mean.

Section Six — Textiles

Properties of Components in Systems

1 A photosensitive material can be used in the production of printed circuit boards (PCBs).

a) What is a photosensitive material?

....

[1 mark]

b) What is used to modify the photosensitive material during PCB production?

....

[1 mark]

2 Some of the components in domestic appliances are frequently exposed to water. For example the inside of the dishwasher, shown in **Figure 1**, comes into contact with water during use.

Name **one** suitable material that parts that are exposed to water could be made of. Give a reason for your answer.

....

....

....

Figure 1

[2 marks]

3 Most electronic components will have a current and voltage rating that is set by the manufacturer.

a) What are current and voltage ratings?

....

....

[1 mark]

b) A bulb has a current rating of 0.03 A and a voltage rating of 1.2 V. Suggest what could happen if a power source supplying a voltage and current much higher than these ratings was used to power the bulb.

....

[1 mark]

4 The properties of aluminium can be modified through a process called anodisation. Aluminium pans are often anodised to make them resistant to scratches.

a) What is applied to the aluminium in order to anodise it?

....

[1 mark]

b) Explain how anodising makes the pan more resistant to scratches.

....

....

....

[2 marks]

5   Electrical heating elements are used in some domestic appliances. They are designed to become hot when an electric current is passed through them. They are often made from a nickel-chromium alloy.

a) Name **one** domestic appliance that you would expect to contain a heating element made from a nickel-chromium alloy.

....

[1 mark]

b) Give **one** property that you would expect a nickel-chromium alloy to have that makes it suitable for use as a heating element. Explain your answer.

....

....

....

[2 marks]

6   Steel is often used in car bodies as it is tough and designed to crumple.

a) Suggest why these are important properties for a car body to have.

....

....

....

[2 marks]

b) Aluminium is used in the bodies of some expensive cars, because it is less dense than steel. Suggest **one** benefit of using a lower density material in car bodies.

....

....

[1 mark]

Score: [   ] / **15**

Exam Practice Tip

When you're in the exam and time is ticking away, it can be easy to skim questions and not read them properly. However, it's worth spending some time to read them carefully and make sure you understand exactly what is being asked. You'll be kicking yourself if you get the wrong end of the stick just because you're rushing...

Section Seven — Electronic and Mechanical Systems

Standard Components in Systems

Warm-Up

Draw lines to match each electronic component on the left with its description.

E12 series   A type of programmable microcontroller.

Programmable intelligent
computer (PIC)   A tiny circuit contained within a single component.

Integrated circuit (IC)   A set of fixed resistors.

1   **Figure 1** shows a Dual in Line package (DIL). This is used to package an integrated circuit (IC).

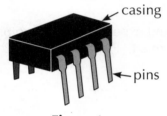

casing

pins

Figure 1

a) State the function of the pins and the casing.

    ....

    ....

    ....
                                                                                                    [2 marks]

b) Give **two** ways that a DIL IC package can be attached to a printed circuit board (PCB).

    1. ....

    ....

    2. ....

    ....
                                                                                                    [2 marks]

2   Programmable intelligent computers (PICs) can have different types of memory.

    Most PICs have flash memory. How do these PICs differ from one-time programmable (OTP) ones?

    ....

    ....

    ....
                                                                                                    [1 mark]

3 The E12 series are fixed resistors.

a) What is the role of a fixed resistor in an electrical circuit?

....
[1 mark]

b) The resistance of an E12 resistor is stated as **56** ohms **±10%**.
Give the range its actual resistance lies within.

....

....

....

....
[3 marks]

c) Coloured bands are used to identify different E12 resistors.
The numbers these bands represent are shown in **Figure 2**.
State the colours of the first **three** bands that would be used to
identify an E12 resistor with a resistance of **68 000** ohms.
The colours must be stated in the correct order.

....

....

....
[1 mark]

Colour of band	Number
Black	0
Brown	1
Red	2
Orange	3
Yellow	4
Green	5
Blue	6
Violet	7
Grey	8
White	9

Figure 2

4 Mechanical components are sold in different shapes and sizes.

a) Give **two** specific characteristics that different types of gears can be sold by.

1. ....

2. ....
[2 marks]

b) **i)** State the **two** major types of springs that can be sold.

1. ....

2. ....
[2 marks]

ii) Give the main difference between these types of springs.

....

....
[1 mark]

Score: [ ] **/15**

Section Seven — Electronic and Mechanical Systems

86

Cutting, Drilling and Soldering

Warm-Up

Use the words in the box to label the diagram of a soldered connection.

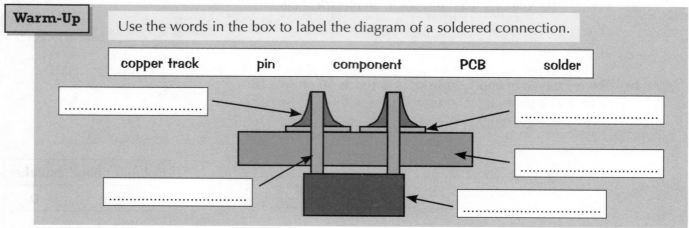

| copper track | pin | component | PCB | solder |

1   Solder is a good electrical conductor.

Why is this an important property for solder to have when it is used to
attach components to a printed circuit board (PCB)?

....

....

[1 mark]

2   Automated soldering methods are used in the mass production of printed circuit boards (PCBs).

Name **one** automated soldering method.

Name: ....

Use sketches and/or notes to give a detailed description of this method.

[5 marks]

Score: ☐ /6

Section Seven — Electronic and Mechanical Systems

PCB Production and Surface Treatments

Warm-Up

Circle the methods that can be used to apply a lacquer to a printed circuit board (PCB).

Pressing   Injecting   Dyeing   Spraying

Dipping   Painting   Soldering   Hammering

---

1 Oil is an example of a lubricant. It is often used in mechanical systems such as car engines.

a) What is the purpose of a lubricant?

....

....
[1 mark]

b) Give **two** benefits of using a lubricant in a mechanical system.

1. ....

....

2. ....

....
[2 marks]

---

2 Pick and place assembly of printed circuit boards (PCBs) can be done by hand or using computer-aided manufacture (CAM) machines.

a) What is meant by pick and place assembly?

....

....
[1 mark]

b) Give **one** advantage and **one** disadvantage of using a pick and place CAM machine to assemble PCBs, compared to carrying out the process manually.

Advantage: ....

....

Disadvantage: ....

....
[2 marks]

3 Printed circuit boards (PCBs) can be treated with a lacquer after the components have been mounted and soldered in place.

a) **i)** What type of material are PCB lacquers made from?

....

[1 mark]

ii) What is the function of a PCB lacquer?

....

....

[1 mark]

b) Some lacquers are fluorescent. This allows the lacquer to be viewed under UV light. Describe how using fluorescent lacquers is useful in the quality control of PCBs during their manufacture.

> Quality control is used to check products have been manufactured to a high enough standard.

....

....

....

[2 marks]

4 Blank printed circuit boards (PCBs) have a layer of copper over the whole board with a layer of photosensitive material on top. Photo-etching is the process that converts a blank PCB into a board with custom copper tracks.

Use sketches and/or notes to give a detailed description of the process of photo-etching.

[4 marks]

Score: [   ] / 14

Looking at the Work of Designers

Warm-Up   Draw lines to connect the designers on the left to the work they're best known for.

Alexander McQueen	Fashion
Gerrit Rietveld	Architecture
Alec Issigonis	Wallpaper, furniture and furnishings
Raymond Templier	Cars
Harry Beck	London Underground map
William Morris	Jewellery

---

1   Briefly describe the work of **one** of the following companies.

• Braun	• Apple®	• Gap	• Primark®
• Dyson™	• Alessi	• ZARA	• Under Armour®

Name of company: ....

You don't need to write loads and loads about the named company you've chosen — just pick out the key points that concisely summarise the work of the company, e.g. what the company make, the style of their products, etc.

....

....

....

....

....

[3 marks]

---

2   Compare the work of **two** of the designers listed below.

In your answer you should try to include what each designer is well-known for, the style(s) they work with, and examples of their work.

• Harry Beck	• Alexander McQueen	
• Vivienne Westwood	• Aldo Rossi	
• Marcel Breuer	• Philippe Starck	• Charles Rennie Mackintosh
• Mary Quant	• Louis Comfort Tiffany	• Gerrit Rietveld
• Norman Foster	• Raymond Templier	• Sir Alec Issigonis
• William Morris	• Coco Chanel	• Ettore Sottsass

[8 marks]

Remember this question is all about comparing two designers, so you'll need to focus on their similarities and differences.

Score: ☐ / 11

Understanding User Needs

1   A new tennis racket is being designed.

Explain **two** ways that anthropometric data could be useful when designing a tennis racket.

1. ....

....

2. ....

....

[2 marks]

2   Products are designed so that they are suitable for most people in their target market. The cash machine in **Figure 1** is designed to suit adults.

a)   Suggest **two** groups of adults that may find it difficult to use the cash machine in **Figure 1**. Give a reason for each answer.

Group 1: ....

Reason: ....

....

[2 marks]

Group 2: ....

Reason: ....

....

[2 marks]

Figure 1

b)   How could the design of the cash machine be altered to make it more suitable for the two groups you mentioned in part **a)**?

Group 1: ....

Group 2: ....

[2 marks]

3   A company is designing a new computer keyboard with an ergonomic design.

a)   Suggest a piece of anthropometric data that could be used to make the keyboard ergonomic.

....

[1 mark]

b)   What might happen to the user of the keyboard if it's not ergonomically designed?

....

[1 mark]

4 Products aimed at different age groups will often have designs that are adapted to suit the **physical capabilities** of that age group. Suggest **one** way in which a pair of shoes designed for children may differ from those designed for adults. Give a reason for your answer.

....

....

....

[2 marks]

5 **Figure 2** shows a design for an adjustable headset.

a) Suggest **two** pieces of anthropometric data that should be considered when designing the headset.

1. ....

....

2. ....

....

[2 marks]

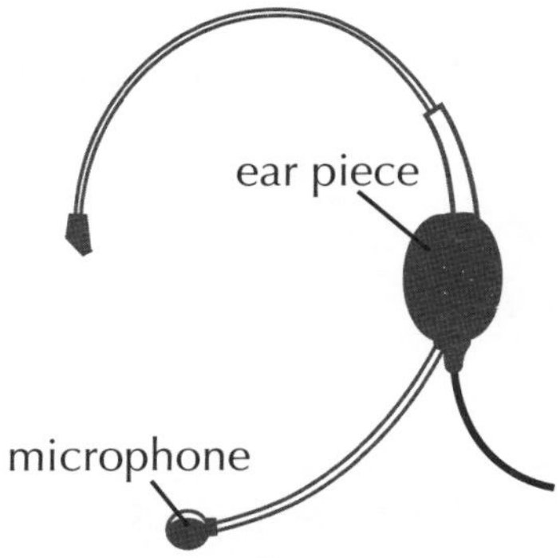

ear piece

microphone

Figure 2

b) The headset is only available in one size. Although it is adjustable, it will not fit a user that falls into the 97th percentile for head size. Explain why.

....

....

....

[2 marks]

6 **Figure 3** shows some anthropometric data for an average 18-40 year old British male. **Figure 4** shows the measurements of a dining chair. All dimensions are in mm. Assess the ergonomics of the chair in **Figure 4** for use by an average 18-40 year old British male.

....

....

....

....

....

....

....

[4 marks]

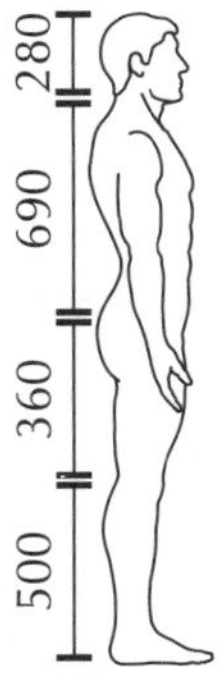

Figure 3

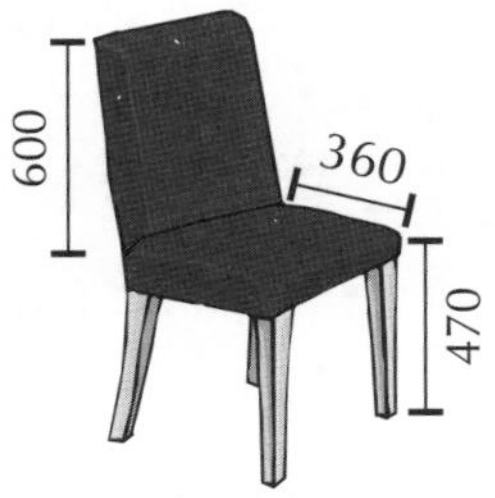

280 690 360 500

600 360 470

Figure 4

Score: _____ / 20

Section Eight — Designing and Making

Design Briefs and Specifications

1   Write a design brief for a product that might help in each of the following situations.

   a)   A plumber has a large number of tools. He spends a lot of time having
   to sort through them to find the right one.

   ....

   ....

   [1 mark]

   b)   Young children can get bored whilst travelling on a long journey.

   ....

   ....

   [1 mark]

2   A company has completed some market research for a new CD rack — the results of part of
   their findings are shown in **Figure 1**. The company has then written a design specification
   (shown in **Figure 2**) for a designer to refer to when designing the CD rack.

   > Results of market research:
   >
   > **Q1**   Average number of CDs that people own = **35**
   >
   > **Q2**   Favourite colour:
   >   Silver **42%**, blue **19%**, red **22%**, pink **7%**, other **10%**

   Figure 1

   > • It must have enough storage.
   > • It must be a nice colour.

   Figure 2

   a)   Explain why these specification points wouldn't help the designer.

   ....

   ....

   [1 mark]

   b)   Suggest a rewording for the **two** specification points in **Figure 2** so that they are more helpful.
   You should include an explanation as to how each point has been decided upon.

   Point 1:   ....

   ....

   [2 marks]

   Point 2:   ....

   ....

   [2 marks]

3 A pet accessories company are designing a new product. The design brief is shown in **Figure 3**.

> Design a high quality cage for pet mice to live outside in all year round.
> There are currently very few commercially available products that do this.
> The cage will be sold to owners that want to keep their mice outdoors.

Figure 3

The company are thinking about carrying out some research for their product.

a) **i)** Give **two** reasons why the company would want to carry out research.

1. ....

2. ....

[2 marks]

ii) The company decide to carry out some market research. Name **one** other type of research that could be carried out by the company, and describe what it would involve.

....

....

[2 marks]

b) **Figures 4** and **5** show the findings from the market research.

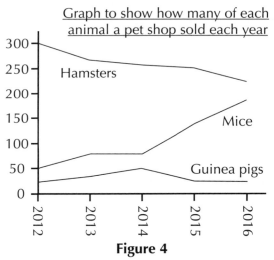

Graph to show how many of each animal a pet shop sold each year

Figure 4

- 87% of people who have mice as pets say they keep their mice indoors.
- 18% of all owners say they would keep their mice indoors all the time if they had a choice.
- Of the people who keep their mice outside, 98% say they only keep the cage outside during the summer, as this is the only time when it is a comfortable temperature for the mice.
- Experts say the cage needs to be well-ventilated, so a wire mesh is best for cage walls. Well-ventilated cages are very difficult to heat though.

Figure 5

i) State **two** conclusions that can be drawn from **Figure 4**.

1. ....

2. ....

[2 marks]

ii) The conclusions of the market research have led the company to reconsider the design brief. Suggest **one** change that should be made to the design brief. Give a reason for your answer.

....

....

....

[2 marks]

Score: ☐/14

Market Research

1 Designs are often aimed at specific target markets.

a) **i)** What is a target market?

....

[1 mark]

ii) Target markets can be defined by age or lifestyle.
Give **two** other ways in which a target market can be defined.

1. ....

2. ....

[2 marks]

b) Identify a possible target market for the pin-striped suit shown in **Figure 1**.
Explain your answer.

....

....

[2 marks]

Figure 1

2 A company are carrying out some market research for a computer games carry case that they are designing. They received 25 responses to their questionnaire. These are summarised in **Figure 2**.

> Results of market research:
>
> **Q1** Average number of hours spent on computer per week = **12**
>
> **Q2** Average number of computer games they'd want to transport at once = **5**
>
> **Q3** Most common size of computer game = **19 cm x 14 cm**
>
> **Q4** How often they take their games to a friend's house per week:
> less than once **32%**, once **36%**, twice **20%**, 3 times **8%**, 4 or more times **4%**

Figure 2

a) Describe how these findings would affect the design of the product.

....

....

....

[2 marks]

b) Suggest **two** additional questions for this market research that haven't been answered by the results shown in **Figure 2**. Give **one** closed question and **one** open question.

Closed question: ....

....

[1 mark]

Section Eight — Designing and Making

Open question: ....

....

[1 mark]

c) The company wants to present the results from **Figure 2 Q4** as a pie chart.
    Complete the pie chart shown in **Figure 3** to show these results. You must show your working.

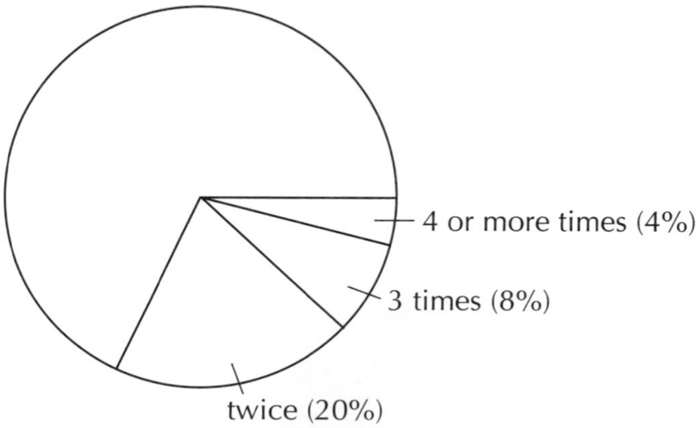

— 4 or more times (4%)

3 times (8%)

twice (20%)

Figure 3

Use this space to show your working.

....

....

....

[2 marks]

d) The makers of the carry case want to carry out further research
    using interviews and focus groups.

   i) Suggest **one** advantage of using interviews rather than questionnaires
       during market research.

   ....

   ....

   [1 mark]

   ii) Why can audio recordings be useful during an interview?

   ....

   ....

   [1 mark]

   iii) What is the aim of a focus group?

   ....

   ....

   [1 mark]

Score: ☐/**14**

Section Eight — Designing and Making

Product Analysis

Draw circles to show whether the statements below are **true** or **false**.

Product analysis can be done by looking at the outside of a product or taking it apart.   True / False

Ergonomics is about designing products so they can be packaged easily.   True / False

Aesthetics is the general appearance of a product.   True / False

1   A kitchen equipment company plans to design a new kettle. **Figure 1** shows two existing products.

Product 1   Product 2

Max

Min

plastic

metal base

Figure 1

Analyse the two products shown in **Figure 1** in terms of their:

There isn't one right answer for this question — you just need to say what you think about the two kettle designs.

a)   functionality

Product 1: ....

....

Product 2: ....

....

[2 marks]

b)   aesthetics

Product 1: ....

....

Product 2: ....

....

[2 marks]

c)   ergonomics

Product 1: ....

....

Product 2: ....

....

[2 marks]

2   A company are designing a low cost, winter coat for women, made from environmentally-friendly materials. **Figure 2** shows an example of a women's winter coat already on the market.

Analyse the product shown in **Figure 2** in terms of:

You may need to use your knowledge on materials to help you answer these questions.

a)   its functionality

....

....

....

....

....

....

[2 marks]

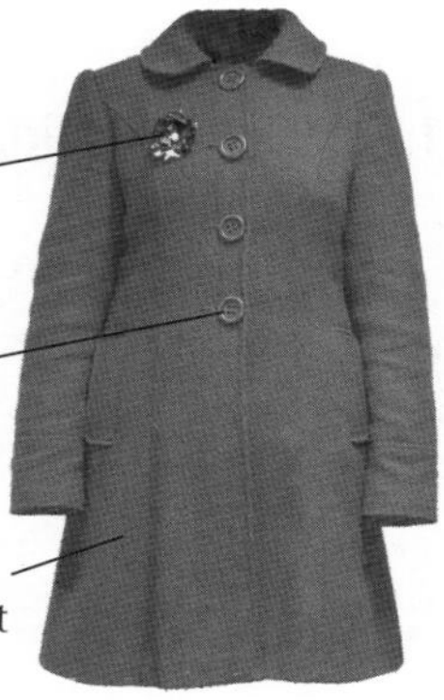

b)   the cost of its materials

metal brooch

recycled plastic buttons

nylon with a water-resistant finish

Figure 2

....

....

....

....

[2 marks]

c)   the sustainability of its materials

....

....

....

[2 marks]

d)   The company are also trying to minimise the negative social impact of their garments.

State **two** negative social impacts that they could try and avoid during the manufacture of their new coat.

....

....

....

[2 marks]

Score: [   ] /**14**

Section Eight — Designing and Making

Design Strategies

Draw lines to connect the words on the left with their definitions on the right.

Systems approach — A design strategy that involves breaking down the design process into a number of different stages, and doing each one in turn.

User-centred design — A situation where the designer gets stuck on a particular idea when designing a product.

Design fixation — A design strategy in which the wants and needs of the user are prioritised throughout the design process.

1 Collaborating with other people is important throughout the design process.

State **two** groups of people that a designer could collaborate with.
Explain how collaboration could be useful in each case.

1. ....

....

....

2. ....

....

....

[4 marks]

2 Iterative design is a strategy centred around a constant process of evaluation and improvement.

Use sketches and/or notes to give a detailed description of the iterative design process.

[4 marks]

Score: ___ /8

Section Eight — Designing and Making

Exploring and Developing a Design Idea

1 The design for a new child's toy boat is shown in **Figure 1**.

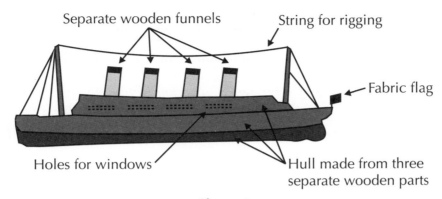

Figure 1

a) Models are useful for visualising designs in 3D and identifying problems with a design.
Give **two** other reasons why a model might be built.

1. ....

....

2. ....

....

[2 marks]

b) Suggest a suitable material to model the ship in. Explain your answer.

....

....

[2 marks]

c) A simple electronic circuit could be used to light up the windows of the boat.
Name a piece of equipment that could be used to test this circuit.

....

[1 mark]

2 A seamstress is designing a one-off dress for a client. She is in the process of making a toile.

a) Describe how a toile could be used to improve the design of the dress.

....

....

....

[2 marks]

b) **i)** It's important for the fabric used to make a toile to have similar properties (e.g. stretchiness) to the fabric that will be used to make the real garment.
State **two** other properties that a toile fabric should have, and give a reason for each one.

1. ....

....

2. ....

....

[4 marks]

ii) Name a material that is commonly used as a toile fabric.

....

[1 mark]

3 A company is designing a new milk carton aimed at young children. The carton will hold 200 ml of milk. A detailed sketch of the carton design is shown in **Figure 2**.

a) The company has made a model of the carton shown in **Figure 2**. What should this model be tested and evaluated against?

....

....

[1 mark]

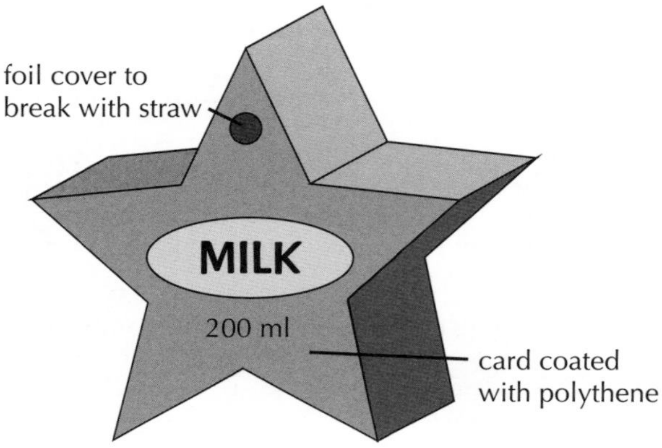

foil cover to
break with straw

MILK

200 ml

card coated
with polythene

Figure 2

b) Suggest a test that could be carried out on the model.

....

....

[1 mark]

c) During the testing and evaluation of the model, the design was found to be too costly to make. Suggest why this might be the case, and give a suggestion to reduce the cost of manufacture.

....

....

....

[2 marks]

d) After a successful model has been made, what is the next stage in the design process?

....

[1 mark]

Score: ⬚ /19

Section Eight — Designing and Making

Drawing Techniques

1 Isometric drawing is one way to present designs.

a) What are isometric drawings used to show?

....
[1 mark]

b) Using the isometric grid below, produce an isometric drawing of a
box that is 30 mm wide, 40 mm deep and 20 mm high.

10 mm

[2 marks]

2 System diagrams and schematic diagrams are often drawn for electronic and mechanical systems.

a) What is a system diagram?

....
[1 mark]

b) How do schematic diagrams differ from system diagrams?

....

....

....
[2 marks]

c) Give **one** example of a schematic diagram.

....
[1 mark]

d) Give **two** reasons why schematic diagrams are often simplified and not drawn to scale.

1. ....

2. ....
[2 marks]

Section Eight — Designing and Making

3   Perspective drawing is a type of three-dimensional drawing.

a)   Give **one** advantage of drawing in perspective.

....

....

[1 mark]

b)   **Figure 1** shows a design for a tissue box.
Make a one-point perspective drawing of the tissue box.

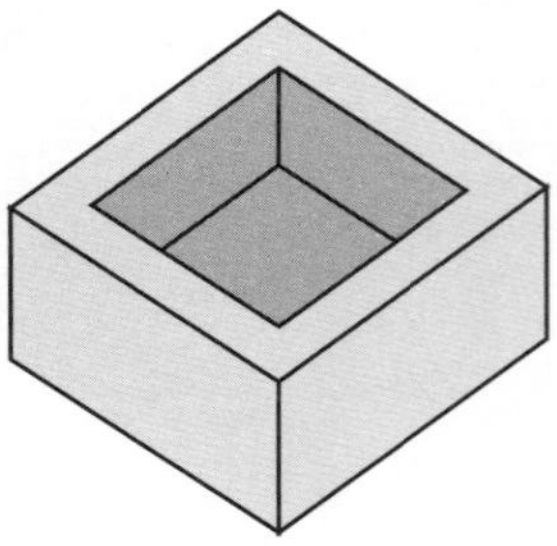

Figure 1

[2 marks]

c)   **Figure 2** shows a design for a lampshade.
Using two-point perspective, redraw the lamp shade as it would look if it was above the horizon.

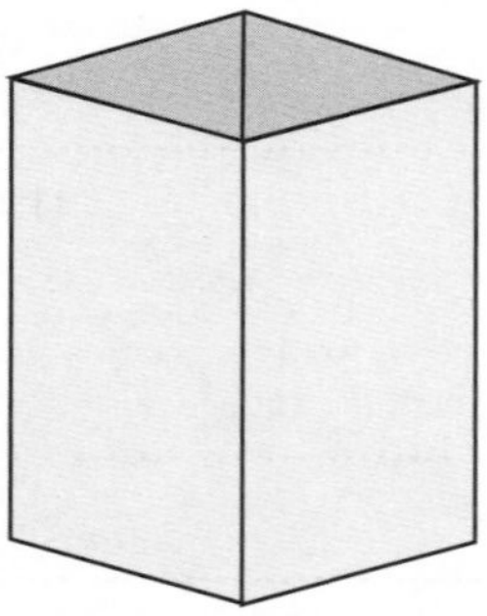

Figure 2

[3 marks]

Score: [   ] **/15**

> **Exam Practice Tip**
>
> In the exam, you should do any drawings and sketches using a sharp pencil. It might be a good idea to draw lightly at first, as this will make it much easier to rub out any mistakes you make. Then once you're happy with your drawing, you can quickly go over it again to make sure that your final answer is clear for the examiner to see.

Section Eight — Designing and Making

More on Drawing Techniques

1 The bookcase in **Figure 1** needs to be assembled at home by the consumer. Instructions are needed to help the consumer assemble it.

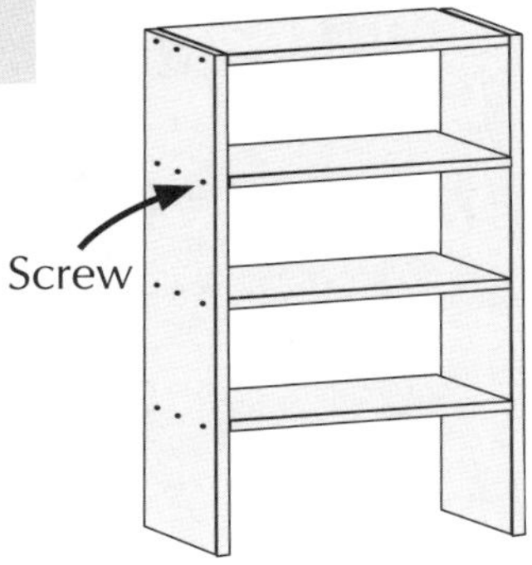

a) Name the style of drawing that would be most suitable for the instructions. Explain why this style of drawing is suitable.

Name: ....

Explanation: ....

....

[2 marks]

Figure 1

Screw

b) Draw assembly instructions for the bookcase using this style of drawing.

[3 marks]

2 A company have produced a scale drawing of a table for a client.

a) The table will have a width of 1.25 m. The scale drawing of the table has a width of 25 cm. Calculate the scale of the drawing. Give your answer as a ratio in its simplest form.

....

....

....

[2 marks]

b) The scale drawing of the table has a height of 18 cm. What will its real height be?

....

....

[1 mark]

Section Eight — Designing and Making

3   **Figure 2** shows a design for a toaster.

a)   Complete **Figure 2** by naming the two other views that are shown in a third angle orthographic projection.

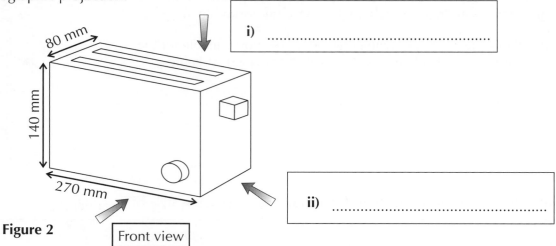

i) ....

ii) ....

Figure 2

Front view

[2 marks]

b)   Complete the following third angle orthographic projection of the toaster shown in **Figure 2**.

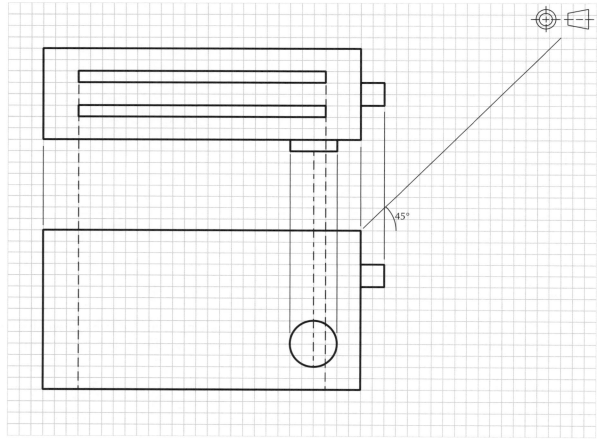

45°

[3 marks]

Score: ☐ / **13**

Exam Practice Tip

When drawing a third angle orthographic projection, you might find it useful to make a list of all of the features that you can see on the object. All of these features should be marked on each view in some way — as outlines if they can be seen, or as hidden details if they can't — so you can tick them off the list once you've finished drawing. Remember to label the drawing with dimensions too (if they're given in the question).

Section Eight — Designing and Making

 ☐   ☐   ☺ ☐

Manufacturing Specification

1 A Christmas card design has a Christmas tree hanging in a window. **Figure 1** shows the tools and components needed. **Figure 2** shows the inside and front of a finished card. The card is to be made on a large scale using a manufacturing specification.

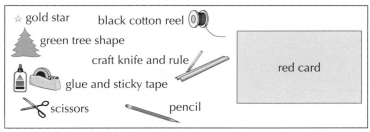

Figure 1

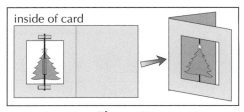

Figure 2

a) Sequence diagrams such as flowcharts can be used in a manufacturing specification. Draw a flow chart that shows an assembly process that could be used to make the card. Include at least **one** quality control check.

Start

[3 marks]

b) The specification will be written using the information in **Figure 1**, **Figure 2** and the flowchart of the assembly process. Give **two** additional pieces of information that would need to be included in the manufacturing specification for the card.

1. ....

2. ....

[2 marks]

2 A designer has written a manufacturing specification for a shirt.

a) Give **two** pieces of information about the shirt fabric that could be in this specification.

1. ....

2. ....

[2 marks]

b) Give **two** pieces of information about manufacturing the shirt that could be in this specification.

1. ....

2. ....

[2 marks]

3 **Figure 3** shows a storage box. **Figure 4** shows the manufacturing process for making one box.

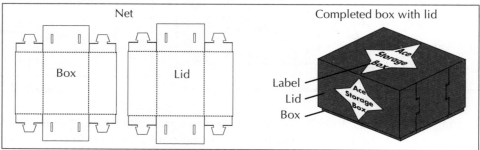

Figure 3

	5 min	10 min	15 min	20 min	25 min	30 min	35 min	40 min	45 min	50 min	55 min	60 min	65 min	70 min	75 min	80 min	85 min
Mark out net	■	■	■														
Cut out the box and lid				■													
Paint the box						■	■										
Allow the paint to dry								■	■	■							
Paint the lid											■						
Allow the paint to dry												■	■	■			
Apply the labels to the lid															■		
Assemble the box and lid																■	

Figure 4

a) Name the type of sequence diagram shown in **Figure 4**.

....

[1 mark]

b) **i)** Using this sequence diagram, state how long it should take to paint the box.

....

[1 mark]

ii) How long should it take to manufacture the storage box from start to finish?

....

[1 mark]

c) Suggest **one** change that could be made to the manufacturing process to reduce the total time it takes. Explain your reasoning.

....

....

[1 mark]

Score: ⬚ / **13**

Developing Prototypes

1   A designer has made a prototype of a tent. The prototype is shown in **Figure 1**.

Give **three** possible reasons why a prototype of the tent was made.

1. ....

....

2. ....

....

3. ....

....

[3 marks]

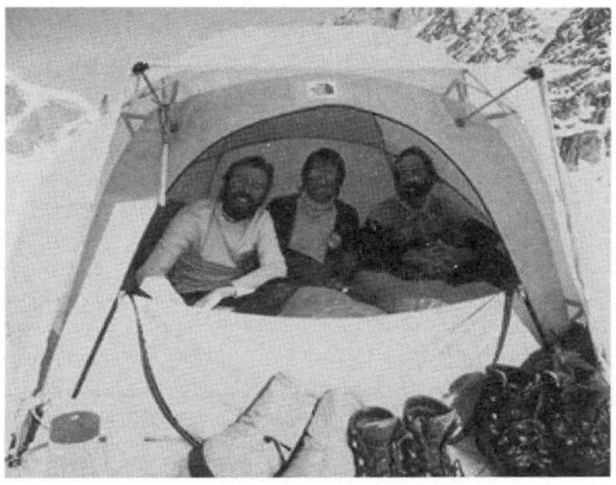

Figure 1

2   A designer has made a prototype of a label for a shampoo bottle.
Figure 2 shows the design specification. **Figure 3** shows the prototype.

The label should:
* show the name of the product and what it smells of
* have a futuristic or scientific appearance
* include an image of glossy hair

Figure 2

GLOSSYMAX

Figure 3

Evaluate the prototype of the label against the design specification.

Remember, 'evaluating' a prototype
against a specification means
checking whether each point on the
specification is met by the prototype.

....

....

....

....

....

[4 marks]

3   **Figure 4** shows a prototype for a children's coat.
      Figure 5 shows the design specification for the coat.

Figure 4

Design specification
- it must appeal to children
- it must be a winter coat
- it must include a way of fastening the coat
- it must be highly visible for road safety purposes

Figure 5

a)   Which **two** points on the design specification might the prototype not meet?
     Give a reason for each point.

     1.   ....

     ....

     2.   ....

     ....
                                                                                                              [2 marks]

b)   For each point stated in **a)**, suggest **one** improvement that could be made.

     1.   ....

     ....

     2.   ....

     ....
                                                                                                              [2 marks]

c)   How could the designer see if the changes suggested in part **b)** improve the product?

     ....

     ....

     ....
                                                                                                              [2 marks]

d)   When can production of the coat on a larger scale be considered?

     ....

     ....
                                                                                                              [1 mark]

Score: [   ] / **14**

Section Eight — Designing and Making

 [ ]   [ ]   ☺ [ ]

Using Materials Efficiently

Warm-Up

A range of tools and equipment used in marking out are listed below.
Draw lines to match each tool with the description of how it is used in marking out.

Odd-leg caliper	Used to transfer markings onto a fabric that you can remove later.
Try square	Drawn around to mark out the same shape.
Scriber	Marks a line parallel to an edge.
Tailor's chalk	Used like a pencil to scratch a mark into metal and plastic.
Templates	Helps to accurately mark out right angles.

1   When batch or mass producing a product, identical shapes are often cut from sheets of material. Careful planning of an efficient arrangement for these shapes can help to minimise waste.

a) What is the name of this planning process?

....
[1 mark]

b) Give **two** reasons why manufacturers try to avoid wasting materials.

1. ....

2. ....
[2 marks]

c) Explain how using a design that tessellates can help to reduce waste.

....

....
[2 marks]

d) Show that the shape in the box below will tessellate.

[1 mark]

Section Eight — Designing and Making

2 Marking out is one way of reducing the waste produced when making a product.

Explain how marking out can help to reduce waste.

....

....

....

[2 marks]

3 A manufacturer is cutting blocks from a piece of wood that measures 5 × 5 × 240 cm.

He is able to use 5775 cm³ of the material. What volume of waste material will he have?

....

....

[2 marks]

4 Triangles are to be cut from the sheet of material shown in **Figure 1**. The triangles need to be arranged so that as many of them as possible can be cut from the sheet.

a) Repeat the triangle shown in **Figure 1** to show the arrangement that results in the least possible waste material.

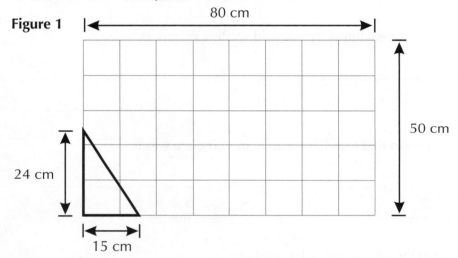

Figure 1 — 80 cm, 50 cm, 24 cm, 15 cm

[1 mark]

b) Calculate the area of **one** triangle.

....

....

[1 mark]

c) Using your answers to **a)** and **b)**, calculate the minimum amount of material wasted from cutting the triangles from the sheet in **Figure 1**.

....

....

[3 marks]

Score: ⬚ / **15**

Section Eight — Designing and Making

Working Safely

1   **Figure 1** shows a man cutting wood using a circular saw.

Give **two** things he should do to carry out the task more safely.

1. ....

2. ....

[2 marks]

Figure 1

2   Safety is vital when designing and manufacturing a product.

a)   Suggest **one** piece of protective clothing or equipment that should be worn when carrying out each of the following activities:

i)   Tacking a fabric using a needle and thread.

....

[1 mark]

ii)   Drilling with a piece of noisy machinery.

....

[1 mark]

iii)   Sanding a material that produces a lot of dust.

....

[1 mark]

b)   Other than wearing appropriate protective clothing, give **one** safety precaution that should be taken when handling toxic chemicals.

....

[1 mark]

c)   Other than wearing appropriate protective clothing, give **two** general safety rules that should be followed when operating machine tools.

1. ....

2. ....

[2 marks]

3   Risk assessments are used to identify and minimise any risks when working.

Give **one** hazard of welding and **one** precaution that could be taken to reduce this risk.

Hazard: ....

Precaution: ....

[2 marks]

Score: ☐ /**10**

  ☐   ☐   ☐

Section Eight — Designing and Making

Section Nine — Mixed Questions

1   Which **one** of the following is used to coat metals in the process of galvanisation?

    A   PVC   ☐

    B   Zinc   ☐

    C   Aluminium   ☐

    D   Nickel   ☐

[1 mark]

2   Which **one** of the following statements is true?

    A   Non-ferrous metals contain iron.   ☐

    B   Oak is a softwood.   ☐

    C   Tracing paper is used for packaging.   ☐

    D   High-density polyethylene is a thermoforming plastic.   ☐

[1 mark]

3   Which **one** of the following describes oscillating motion?

    A   Moving one way in a straight line.   ☐

    B   Moving backwards and forwards in an arc.   ☐

    C   Moving backwards and forwards in a straight line.   ☐

    D   Moving in a circle.   ☐

[1 mark]

4   Which **one** of the following statements is **not** true?

    A   Foil-lined board has an aluminium foil lining and is used to package food.   ☐

    B   Cotton fabric is made into denim, which is used to make jeans.   ☐

    C   Ash is a softwood used in tool handles and baseball bats.   ☐

    D   Graphene is an extremely thin layer of graphite,
and is used in products such as tennis rackets.   ☐

[1 mark]

5   Which **one** of the following statements about the cam shown in **Figure 1** is true?

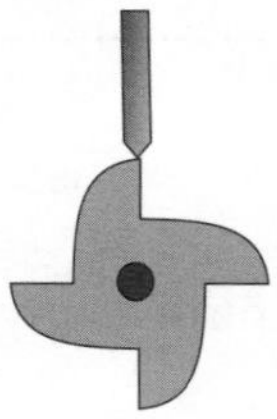

Figure 1

    A   As the cam rotates, the follower will rise and then suddenly fall.   ☐

    B   The cam can be rotated in both directions.   ☐

    C   For each whole turn of the cam, the follower will move up and down twice.   ☐

    D   As the cam rotates, the follower will gently rise and then gently fall.   ☐

[1 mark]

6   **Figure 2** shows a range of different items.

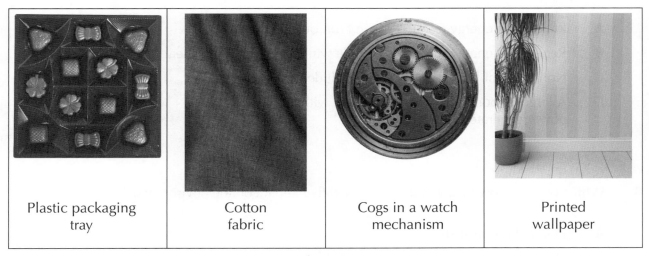

| Plastic packaging tray | Cotton fabric | Cogs in a watch mechanism | Printed wallpaper |

Figure 2

Choose **one** of the items shown in **Figure 2**.
Name a process that is used to manufacture your chosen item.

Process: ....

In the box below, use sketches and/or notes to give a
detailed description of this manufacturing process.

[5 marks]

7 Which **one** of the following statements is **not** true?

    A   Renewable energy resources won't run out. ☐

    B   Renewable energy resources include wind, sunlight and nuclear fuel. ☐

    C   Non-renewable energy resources include coal, oil and gas. ☐

    D   A large carbon footprint is associated with
          power generated using fossil fuels. ☐

[1 mark]

8 Which of the following generally has a **negative** impact on the environment?

    A   Planned obsolescence ☐

    B   Design for disassembly ☐

    C   Design for maintenance ☐

    D   Lean manufacturing ☐

[1 mark]

9 For **one** of the items listed below, name a suitable finish or treatment
that could be applied. Give a brief description of how your chosen
finish/treatment is applied and a reason for your choice of finish/treatment.

> • A book cover
>
> • A garden shed
>
> • The metal handle of a tool
>
> • A 2000 metre roll of plain cotton
>
> • A printed circuit board (PCB) in an air
>   conditioning unit located outdoors

Chosen item: ....

Finish/treatment: ....

Description: ....

....

....

....

Reason for choice: ....

....

....

[3 marks]

Section Nine — Mixed Questions

10 A company is manufacturing a range of gift boxes. The boxes will have various designs printed onto them. **Figure 3** shows the net of one of the gift boxes in the range.

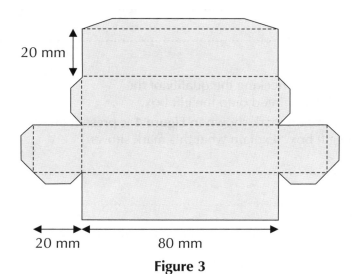

20 mm

20 mm   80 mm

Figure 3

a) On the isometric grid below, produce an isometric drawing of the gift box shown in **Figure 3** when it is assembled.

10 mm

[2 marks]

b) A factory worker is carrying out some quality control checks on an assembled gift box made from the net shown in **Figure 3**.

i) Each dimension of the gift box has a tolerance of ± 1.5 mm.
What is the maximum length that the gift box can be?

....

[1 mark]

ii) The assembled gift box has a height of 21.2 mm, a width of 18.4 mm and a length of 79.1 mm. Explain why this box does **not** fall within the stated tolerance.

....

....

[2 marks]

iii) The factory worker is checking the quality of the design that has been printed onto the gift box.
The colour registration mark shown in **Figure 4** is present on the side of the gift box. Explain what this mark shows.

....

....

....

Figure 4

[2 marks]

c) i) The company has made a prototype of a new type of gift box. The dimensions of the net used for the prototype were marked out by hand. State a production aid that could be used when producing a batch of the new box design to speed up this marking out process.

....

[1 mark]

ii) The nets for this new gift box are cut out from sheets of A1 card, which measure 594 × 841 mm. Each net has an area of 19 200 mm^2, and the manufacturer arranges the nets so that 25 can be cut from one A1 sheet. Calculate the amount of card wasted from each A1 sheet.

....

....

....

[3 marks]

d) The company has been asked to produce a novelty over-sized gift box for a client.
The company's design team has produced a scale drawing of the design for the client.

i) The scale drawing of the box has a height of 15 cm. The box will have a height of 1.5 m.
Calculate the scale of the drawing. Give your answer as a ratio in its simplest form.

....

....

....

[2 marks]

ii) The box will have a length of 390 cm. What will the box length in the scale drawing be?

....

....

[1 mark]

11 A designer has been asked to design a new bed for a company. The company has given her a design brief (shown in **Figure 5**) and asked her to carry out some market research to find out the likes and dislikes of potential users. The results of her market research are shown in **Figure 6**.

> Design a bed that is suitable for someone moving into their first home, as there are not enough affordable options currently available. The bed should be designed to be batch produced.

Figure 5

Q1 What type of bed frame would you prefer?

Type of bed frame	Number of people
Metal	101
Wood	87
Upholstered	172
Total	360

Q2 Would you prefer to have storage built in to the bed's design?
Yes: 78%   No: 18%
Don't mind: 4%

Q3 What size bed are you most likely to buy?
Single: 12%   Double: 71%
King size: 17%

Q4 What amount of money would you expect to spend on a bed?

Price range	Number of people
£0-50	41
£51-100	152
£101-150	113
£151-200	27
£201-250	15
£251-300	7
More than £301	5
Total	360

Figure 6

a) State **one** conclusion that could be drawn from the results of **Q1**, shown in **Figure 6**.

....

....

[1 mark]

b) Describe how the findings of **Q2** and **Q3** in **Figure 6** should affect the design of the product.

Q2: ....

....

Q3: ....

....

[2 marks]

c) From the results of **Q4**, the designer concludes that people would generally expect to pay £150 or less for a bed. Calculate the exact percentage of people who have said this.

....

....

....

[1 mark]

Section Nine — Mixed Questions

d) A possible design for the bed is shown in **Figure 7**.

Complete the following third angle orthographic projection of the design shown in **Figure 7**.

Use the information in **Figure 7** to label the dimensions of the bed in your projection. Some are already shown on the plan view below.

not to scale

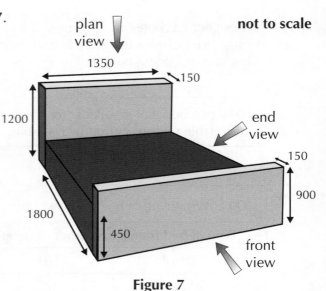

Figure 7

> You'll need to have all the dimensions shown in Figure 7 in your projection to get all of the marks for this question.

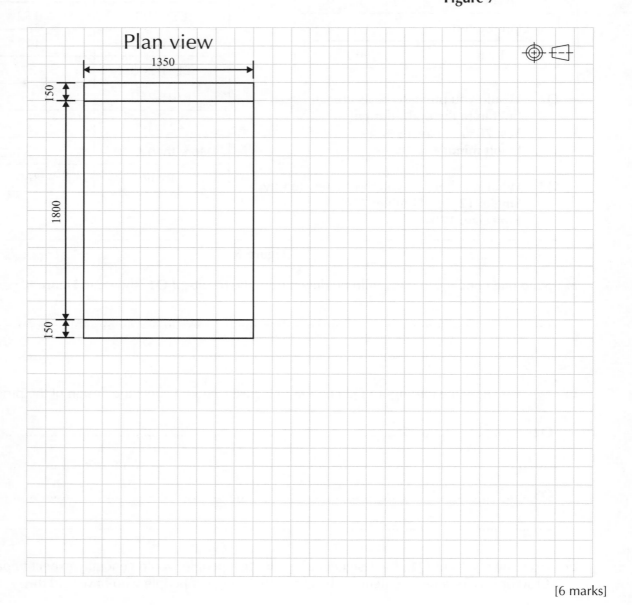

[6 marks]

e) The designer is looking at some anthropometric data to make sure her bed design will fit the target market. State **one** piece of anthropometric data that she should consider.

....

[1 mark]

Section Nine — Mixed Questions

f) The designer is finding it hard to design a bed that could be batch produced for less than £150. She suggests to the company that the design brief should be changed, so that the beds are designed for mass production instead.

Suggest **two** reasons why beds that are mass produced can be sold more cheaply than batch produced beds.

1. ....

....

2. ....

....

[2 marks]

12 A toy manufacturer wants to increase its range of products to include garden toys. The company intends to redesign one of their existing products — the wooden building block set shown in **Figure 8** — by increasing its size and making it suitable for outdoor use.

Figure 8

a) The company is considering making the blocks for the new set from plastic instead of wood.

For safety reasons, the new blocks need to be able to withstand the different forces that act on them when they are in use. Force A acts on the blocks when they are stacked in a tower. Name Force A shown in **Figure 8**.

....
[1 mark]

b) After carrying out research, the company decide to make the new blocks from high-density polyethylene (HDPE).

Give **two** reasons why using this plastic for the blocks may mean that overall the product is less sustainable than if the blocks were made from wood.

1. ....

....

2. ....

....

[2 marks]

Section Nine — Mixed Questions

c) Part of the design specification for the new product is shown in **Figure 9**.

> • The blocks should be strong enough to support the weight of other blocks that are placed on top of them.
> • The blocks should be scaled up versions of the original set.
> • A single block should be light enough for young children to carry.

Figure 9

Suggest **two** additional points to those listed in **Figure 9** that could be included in the design specification. Give a reason for each of your suggestions.

1. ....

....

2. ....

....

[4 marks]

d) A prototype of the product was made and some children were allowed to play with it.

i) What is the definition of a prototype?

....

....

[2 marks]

ii) **Figure 10** shows some feedback from parents of children who tried out the prototype.

> "The blocks were light enough, but they were too large for my child to hold."
>
> "My child quickly got bored of building towers — I think if she could have built different structures she would have played with it for longer."
>
> "I really liked the product but I think it would be too large to store."
>
> "My child really enjoyed playing with the blocks and I thought they were good value for money."

Figure 10

Describe **two** modifications that could be made to the product's design in response to the feedback. Give a reason for each of your suggestions.

1. ....

....

....

2. ....

....

....

[4 marks]

iii) Who else could the company get feedback from about the prototype?

....

[1 mark]

Section Nine — Mixed Questions

13 Briefly describe the work of **one** of the following designers.

- Harry Beck
- Vivienne Westwood
- Marcel Breuer
- Mary Quant
- Norman Foster

- William Morris
- Alexander McQueen
- Aldo Rossi
- Philippe Starck
- Louis Comfort Tiffany

- Raymond Templier
- Coco Chanel
- Charles Rennie Mackintosh
- Gerrit Rietveld
- Sir Alec Issigonis
- Ettore Sottsass

Name of designer: ....

Description: ....

....

....

....

....

[3 marks]

14 Standard components are frequently used in the manufacture of products.

Choose **one** of the products in the box below.

| Paper catalogue | Wooden cupboard | Coat | Bicycle |

Name a suitable standard component that could be used in your chosen product.

Product: ....

Standard component: ....

In the box below, use sketches and/or notes to give a detailed description
of how the standard component is used.

[4 marks]

Section Nine — Mixed Questions

15   **Figure 11** shows a pair of gloves for use in cold conditions that allow the wearer to use a touch screen device (e.g. a smartphone) whilst wearing them.
A clothing company is looking at designing a new range of these gloves.

Figure 11

The gloves work because they have patches of material in the fingertips that contain conductive thread.

a)   Suggest a type of material this thread could be made from. Explain your answer.

....

....

[2 marks]

b)   Give **one** reason why the conductive thread only needs to be present in the fingertips of the gloves.

....

....

[1 mark]

c)   The company is working out costings for the new gloves.
Lengths of conductive thread are available from several different suppliers.
Each length of thread is supplied on a plastic cone.

i)   Complete the table below to calculate the cost per metre for each supplier.

[1 mark]

Supplier	Length of thread per cone (m)	Cost of cone (£)	Cost per metre (£)
A	1650	246.50	0.15
B	1000	40.00	
C	2250	202.50	

ii) One of the designs for the gloves uses 65 cm of conductive thread in each pair.
Calculate the total cost of thread that would be needed to make 7000 pairs of gloves if the thread was purchased from supplier A.

....

....

....

[3 marks]

iii) Explain how ordering the thread in a few large shipments, rather than in many smaller shipments, could help to reduce the carbon footprint of the gloves.

....

....

....

....

[4 marks]

d) The company are considering what material to make the main body of the gloves from. They have decided that wool and polyamide are suitable materials.

i) These materials are both good thermal insulators. Suggest why this makes them suitable for the main body of the gloves.

....

....

[1 mark]

ii) What are the raw materials used to make wool and synthetic polyamide yarns?

Wool ....

Synthetic polyamide ....

[2 marks]

iii) Give **two** reasons why obtaining the raw material needed to make a synthetic polyamide can negatively impact the environment.

1. ....

....

2. ....

....

[2 marks]

iv) Choose **one** of the raw materials you named in part **d) ii)**. Use sketches and/or notes to give a detailed description of how it is converted to yarn.

Raw material: ....

[4 marks]

Section Nine — Mixed Questions

e) The company is thinking of having two different sizes of the gloves in their range.
It plans to target a smaller size at children (ages 12-15) and a larger size at adults (ages 16+).
The measurements used for each of these glove designs is the average for each target group.

i) What percentile represents the average?

....
[1 mark]

ii) Suggest **two** pieces of anthropometric data that the company would need to
obtain average values for to work out the sizes the gloves should be.

1. ....

2. ....
[2 marks]

16 A designer is gathering ideas for a new lamp. **Figure 12** shows a lamp with a leaded glass shade that the designer has found during her research of existing products.

a) Analyse the lamp shown in **Figure 12** in terms of its form.

....

....

....
[1 mark]

Figure 12

b) The designer decides to make a lamp similar to the one shown in **Figure 12**.
The lamp shade is made of many individually cut pieces of glass and is assembled by hand.

i) The designer intends to make the lamps to order.
Which scale of production is appropriate for the lamp shades?

....
[1 mark]

ii) Glass that has been recycled will be used in the lamp shade. Give **two** reasons
why this could make the lamp more sustainable than if new glass were used.

1. ....

....

2. ....

....
[2 marks]

iii) The base of the lamp will be made from bronze.
This is a metal that is mainly made from copper, but it also contains other metals such as tin.

What name is given to metals (e.g. bronze) that contain more than one type of metal?

....
[1 mark]

Score: ☐ /**91**

Section Nine — Mixed Questions

TAQ41